Through Golden Windows

Mostly Magic

Fun and Fantasy

Wonderful Things Happen

Adventures Here and There

Good Times Together

Children Everywhere

Stories of Early America

American Backgrounds

Wide, Wonderful World

Man and His World

THROUGH GOLDEN WINDOWS

Edited by

Nora Beust, M.A.

Phyllis Fenner, B.A., B.L.S.

Bernice E. Leary, PH.D.

Mary Katherine Reely, B.A.

Dora V. Smith, PH.D.

Man and His World

Editor-in-Chief
Jeanne Hale, B.A.
Assistant Editor
Muriel Johnstone, B.A.

Grolier
INCORPORATED
NEW YORK

Standard Book Number 7172-1450-8

Library of Congress Catalog Card Number: 58-5038

Acknowledgments
and Copyright Notice

FOLLETT PUBLISHING COMPANY, – "The Ocean and Its Work," from *How the Earth Is Changing* by Rudolph Bretz, Copyright, 1936, by Follett Publishing Company; "Thunder and Lightning," from *The World's Moods* by Maryanna Heile, Copyright, 1930, by Follett Publishing Company; "The First Metal Workers," from *How the World Grew Up* by Grace Kiner, Copyright, 1930, by Follett Publishing Company; "Man-Made Plants," from *The Garden of the World* by Janet McGill, Copyright, 1930, by Follett Publishing Company. Reprinted by permission of Follett Publishing Company.

HARCOURT, BRACE AND COMPANY, INC., – "Volcanoes and Earthquakes," from *The Sky Is Blue* by W. Maxwell Reed, Copyright, 1940, by Harcourt, Brace and Company, Inc.; "The Storm" by Richard and Louis Untermeyer, and "The Butterfly and the Caterpillar" by Joseph Lauren, from *Rainbow in the Sky,* edited by Louis Untermeyer, Copyright, 1935, by Harcourt, Brace and Company, Inc.; "In Spring" by Michael Lewis, from *Stars to Steer By,* edited by Louis Untermeyer, Copyright, 1941, by Harcourt, Brace and Company, Inc.; "Children of the Wind," from *The People, Yes* by Carl Sandburg, Copyright, 1936, by Harcourt, Brace and Company, Inc.; "Insect Music," with four illustrations, from *The Grasshopper Book,* written and illustrated by Wilfrid S. Bronson, Copyright, 1943, by Harcourt, Brace and Company, Inc.; "What Is an Ant?," with two illustrations, from *The Wonder World of Ants,* written and illustrated by Wilfrid S. Bronson, Copyright, 1937, by Harcourt, Brace and Company, Inc. Reprinted by permission of Harcourt, Brace and Company, Inc.

HARPER & BROTHERS, – "Bridges," from *A World to Know* by James S. Tippett, Copyright, 1933, by Harper & Brothers; "A Magic Mineral," from *Asbestos* by Lilian Holmes Strack, Copyright, 1941, by Harper & Brothers; "The Rock That Glowed in the Dark," from *Radium* by Lilian Holmes Strack, Copyright, 1941, by Harper & Brothers. Reprinted by permission of Harper & Brothers.

D. C. HEATH AND COMPANY, – "The Seasons" by Edna L. Sterling, from *English Is Our Language, 6,* Copyright, 1950, by D. C. Heath and Company. One illustration by Clare Bice, from *Plants, Animals and Machines* by Lucy Sprague Mitchell and Margaret Wise Brown, Copyright, 1944, 1955, by D. C. Heath and Company. Reprinted by permission of D. C. Heath and Company.

HOFFMAN, JOHN C., – "June" by Alice Crowell Hoffman, from Wee Wisdom. Reprinted by permission of John C. Hoffman.

HENRY HOLT AND COMPANY, INC., – "Fog," from *Chicago Poems* by Carl Sandburg, Copyright, 1916, by Henry Holt and Company, Inc., 1944 by Carl Sandburg. Reprinted by permission of Henry Holt and Company, Inc.

JUNIOR NATURAL HISTORY MAGAZINE, – *Giant "Eyes"* by Catherine E. Barry, from Junior Natural History Magazine. Reprinted by permission of Junior Natural History Magazine.

NETTIE KING ASSOCIATES, – Two illustrations by Sabra Mallett Kimball, from *Birds in Their Homes* by Addison Webb, published by Garden City Books, Copyright, 1947, by Duenewald Printing Corporation. Reprinted by permission of Nettie King Associates.

ALFRED A. KNOPF, INC., – "Couriers of the Sky," from *Couriers of the Sky* by Mary Graham Bonner, Copyright, 1944, by Alfred A. Knopf, Inc.; "The Vulture," from *Cautionary Verses* by Hilaire Belloc, published by Alfred A. Knopf, Inc. Reprinted by permission of Alfred A. Knopf, Inc.

LEIGHTON, CLARE, – One illustration, from *Country Matters,* written and illustrated by Clare Leighton, Copyright, 1937, by The Macmillan Company. Reprinted by permission of Clare Leighton.

Through Golden Windows

IN A reading world filled with children's books the addition of one more anthology or set of anthologies leads naturally to the question "Why?" We, who compiled *Through Golden Windows,* first asked ourselves that question almost ten years ago. We are still asking it. Always we arrive at the same answer. "The books are needed."

The power of books has long been recognized. And never more than today when material things are assuming increasing importance, and even the simple act of opening a door is fast getting out of human hands; when global and continental distances are shrinking from weeks and days to hours and minutes, and nearness at home means crowded living, crowded schools and play-grounds, crowded streets and highways; when family ties are weakening and children suffer from want of close, two-parent affection and guidance.

What can books give to a child who is growing up in today's curiously complicated world? Many things, we believe, although the evidence is not altogether conclusive. Facts and information, of course, about almost every-thing; understanding of himself and others; confidence and security; fun and laughter; friends and friendships; escape from reality at times, and again the courage to face reality—all these are possible results if the right book is used with the right child in the right way.

But suppose the right book is not available? Crowded living means limited space for books, at home and at school. Or suppose parents and teachers do not know the right book? Many, by their own admission, do not know chil-dren's books well. Must the child's values in reading be left to chance, while he struggles with his everyday problems, or grows up without feeling the full rapture of a good book?

Through Golden Windows grew out of a fear, on the one hand, that chil-dren's needs are not being met well enough through books; and out of a faith, on the other hand, that carefully compiled anthologies, easily accessible, would help teachers and parents do a better job of guiding children's reading.

Such books, we believe, should give children experience—here, there and everywhere. It should give them variety—sober fact and gay fantasy, practical prose and picture-filled poetry, lives of the great and the everyday intimacy of home folks, history of the past and history in the making, high adventure and the small thrills of daily living. It should show them some of the wonders of the earth and sky and the great achievements of great men. It should assure them the safe moorings of home and country, of family and friends. It should give them confidence in themselves and in others, and in a world that, for all its problems, is a wonderful world to grow up in.

To be most useful, each book should be not too large and not too small, not too easy and not too difficult, but "just right" for the child in pre-school and primary grades or in middle and upper grades. Based on children's interests and reading preferences, it should have not too much nor too little of any one type of material, but a balanced content that would invite all readers.

Through Golden Windows, therefore, was made with an eye on the child and his needs and interests at different stages of development. Bound in ten volumes, each book is attractive to look at, comfortable to hold, interesting to read, and easy to talk about.

Taken together, these books represent five large areas of interest: fun and humor, adventure, children everywhere, the story of America, and science. For each area there are two volumes, one for children of pre-school and primary age, and the other for intermediate grade readers. Hence, as a child grows in reading power, he may move from *Mostly Magic* to *Fun and Fantasy,* and satisfy his need for fun in both. Again, for adventure he may enjoy *Wonderful Things Happen* until he is ready for *Adventures Here and There.* His broadening interest in people finds satisfaction first in *Good Times Together* and later in *Children Everywhere.* Similarly, *Stories of Early America* eventually gives way to *American Backgrounds* and *Wide, Wonderful World* to *Man and His World.*

Within each volume, the selections are loosely tied together into related units, in order that a child may pursue an interest in Pets or Pioneers or Plants, for example, without searching for "more." The obvious overlapping of units and of volumes is not without purpose or benefit. Were it possible to organize reading materials into airtight, dark little compartments, *Through Golden Windows* would defeat its purpose to help "the whole child" to live and grow. On the other hand, a free, less exacting organization allows him to find the same inter-relationships and similarities among his reading experiences as exist in his daily life.

Through Golden Windows, then, aims first to satisfy the child, meet his everyday needs and help him find early the absorbing joy of reading. It aims, also, to acquaint teachers with much of the best in children's books. Used as basic reading in a college course in children's literature, *Through Golden Windows* will help to overcome the limitations imposed by a barren reading childhood and give teachers and parents that first security they need to guide children's reading. Beyond such a course lies a whole world of books that teachers will continue to explore, year after year.

It aims, finally, to help parents by providing a basic home library for their children. Here are stories as old as "Once upon a time" and as new as the children themselves. Here are stories and poems to read aloud and to read to one's self in a quiet corner, "to-go-to-sleep-by" and "to-get-up-with," to laugh at and to learn from, to sing and to act, and sometimes to read for no other reason than the fun of doing something together as a family.

It is to children, teachers, and parents everywhere that these books are affectionately dedicated, in the hope that through the pages they may see, as "through golden windows," the rewarding vista of life itself.

BERNICE E. LEARY

xii

Man and His World

O NE of the most interesting things about this wonderful world is that it is always changing. Season follows season, day grows into night, and rain gives way to sun.

In *Man and His World* we are told how weather men use instruments to forecast weather changes, how the Sun affects the Moon and how they both influence the Earth.

Also, we learn how the "wrinkling" of the earth formed hills and mountains; and we explore the wonders of the ocean. We put on diving suits and, walking on the ocean floor, feel the change from rounded pebbles to fine sand. As we go into deeper water, the greenish light from the surface fades and finally we must turn on our electric searchlights. Dark shapes rush at us and we frighten them away with silver "bullets" from our elastic cuffs.

Then we find out how to know the different kinds of trees; what insects make music; how bees make honey and how the ants, like men, form nations. Among the many stories about animals is "The Land Animal That Went to Sea," which tells how the whale's body changed so that now it lives almost entirely in the sea.

Man's part in changing the world is told in the stories of great scientists and inventors—Thomas Alva Edison, Robert Fulton, George Washington Carver, Alexander Graham Bell, Wilbur and Orville Wright, Marie Curie, and others. As you read about them, you will see how each new discovery changes the world, as if by magic. Health is improved, new substances are developed, new forms of energy are released, new crops are raised, and new uses are found for almost everything.

And still more changes will come, from inventions and discoveries yet to be made by the boys and girls of today—the young scientists-in-the-making.

BERNICE E. LEARY

Contents

EARTH AND SKY
Illustration by Ezra Jack Keats

The World Stands Out on Either Side

BY EDNA ST. VINCENT MILLAY   2

Illustrated by George Bobritzky

Across Our Country   BY CARROLL LANE FENTON

AND MILDRED ADAMS FENTON   3

Illustrated by George Bobritzky

My Prairies   BY HAMLIN GARLAND   7

Illustrated by Ernest Crichlow

Fog   BY CARL SANDBURG   8

Illustrated by Gil Miret

The Rivers and the Sea   AN AESOP FABLE   9

Illustrated by Gil Miret

The Ocean and Its Work   BY RUDOLPH BRETZ   10

Illustrated by Ezra Jack Keats

Volcanoes and Earthquakes   BY W. MAXWELL REED   18

Illustrated by Kurt Wiese

Giant "Eyes"   BY CATHERINE E. BARRY   28

Illustrated by Mauro Caputo

The Stars   BY JEROME S. MEYER   30

Illustrated by Emma Landau

Portrait of the Sun   BY ANNE TERRY WHITE   37

Illustrated by Marvin Bileck

Silver   BY WALTER DE LA MARE   44

Illustrated by Mozelle Thompson

The Moon and Her Mother   AN AESOP FABLE   45
Illustrated by Mozelle Thompson

Let's Go to the Moon   BY ARMAND SPITZ   46
Illustrated by Jack Coggins

Cloud Zoo   BY NORMA GILLETT   51
Illustrated by Mozelle Thompson

The Storm   BY RICHARD AND LOUIS UNTERMEYER   52
Illustrated by Susan Perl

Thunder and Lightning   BY MARYANNA HEILE   54
Illustrated by Seymour Fleishman

How We Measure and Observe the Weather

         BY IVAN RAY TANNEHILL   59
Illustrated by Ezra Jack Keats

FROM SEASON TO SEASON
Illustration by Ezra Jack Keats

The Seasons   BY EDNA L. STERLING   70
Illustrated by Barbara Tanner

The Months   BY CHRISTINA ROSSETTI   71
Illustrated by Barbara Tanner

In Spring   BY MICHAEL LEWIS   72
Illustrated by Marie Stern

April Is a Dancer   BY SOLVEIG PAULSON RUSSELL   73
Illustrated by Marie Stern

How to Know the Trees   BY MILLICENT E. SELSAM   74
Illustrated by D. Alexandroff

The Green Grass Growing All Around   OLD RHYME   78
Illustrated by Marie Stern

The Heart of the Tree   BY H. C. BUNNER   80
Illustrated by Marie Stern

June   BY ALICE CROWELL HOFFMAN   81
Illustrated by Jeanyee Wong

Foolish Flowers   BY RUPERT SARGENT HOLLAND   82
Illustrated by Mozelle Thompson

Rain in Summer

          BY HENRY WADSWORTH LONGFELLOW   83
Illustrated by Mozelle Thompson

End of Summer Poem   BY ROWENA BENNETT   84

The Mist and All   BY DIXIE WILLSON   85
Illustrated by Barbara Tanner

Something Told the Wild Geese   BY RACHEL FIELD   86
Illustrated by Robert Lawson

Snowflakes   BY HENRY WADSWORTH LONGFELLOW   87
Illustrated by Robert Lawson

Frost Work   BY NONA KEEN DUFFY   88
Illustrated by D. Alexandroff

ANIMALS—BIG AND SMALL
Illustration by Ezra Jack Keats

Children of the Wind   BY CARL SANDBURG   90
Illustrated by Ezra Jack Keats

Bird Song   BY LAURA E. RICHARDS   92
Illustrated by Sabra Mallett Kimball

A Bird   BY EMILY DICKINSON   93
Illustrated by Sabra Mallett Kimball

Couriers of the Sky   BY MARY GRAHAM BONNER   94
Illustrated by D. Alexandroff

To a Spider   BY ABIGAIL CRESSON   99
Illustrated by Joseph Cellini

The Butterfly and the Caterpillar—*A Fable Old Is
Here Retold*   BY JOSEPH LAUREN   100
Illustrated by Barbara Tanner

Insect Music   BY WILFRID S. BRONSON   102
Illustrated by Wilfrid S. Bronson

They Build with Wax   BY DOROTHY STERLING   108
    Illustrated by D. Alexandroff

What Is an Ant?   BY WILFRID S. BRONSON   115
    Illustrated by Wilfrid S. Bronson

Snakes   BY HERBERT S. ZIM   120
    Illustrated by Elaine Sand

Four Little Foxes   BY LEW SARETT   122
    Illustrated by Robert Frankenberg

Introducing Dinosaurs   BY ROY CHAPMAN ANDREWS   123
    Illustrated by Thomas W. Voter

Lion Adventures   BY CARL AND MARY L. J. AKELEY   128
    Illustrated by Joseph Cellini

Journey for Elephants   BY WILLIAM BRIDGES   136
    Photographs by Henry Goldstein

The Land Animal That Went to Sea
    BY ROY CHAPMAN ANDREWS   146
    Illustrated by Thomas W. Voter

How to Tell the Wild Animals   BY CAROLYN WELLS   153
    Illustrated by Maurice Sendak

The Panther   BY OGDEN NASH   155
    Illustrated by Maurice Sendak

The Lama   BY OGDEN NASH   155
    Illustrated by Maurice Sendak

The Vulture   BY HILAIRE BELLOC   156

The Ostrich Is A Silly Bird   BY MARY E. W. FREEMAN   156
    Illustrated by Ervine Metzl

Habits of the Hippopotamus   BY ARTHUR GUITERMAN   157
    Illustrated by Ervine Metzl

Circus Elephant   BY KATHRYN WORTH   158
    Illustrated by Clare Leighton

The Law of the Jungle   BY RUDYARD KIPLING   159
    Illustrated by Emma Landau

The Story of Wildlife Conservation   BY EDWARD H.
GRAHAM AND WILLIAM R. VAN DERSAL   162
Illustrated by Robert Frankenberg

My Private Natural History Museum

BY HUGH LOFTING   166
Illustrated by Susan Perl

HOW THE WORLD GROWS
Illustration by Ezra Jack Keats

The Scientists and the Bright Design

BY KATHERINE B. SHIPPEN   170
Illustrated by Charles M. Daugherty

A Hundred Years of Inventions

BY LANCELOT HOGBEN   175
Illustrated by Mauro Caputo

These Curious Numbers of Ours

BY DAVID EUGENE SMITH   177
Illustrated by Marjorie Saynor and Kenneth Symonds

Counting Moons   BY RUTH BRINDZE   180
Illustrated by Helene Carter

The First Metal Workers   BY GRACE KINER   186
Illustrated by Ezra Jack Keats

Man-Made Plants   BY JANET MCGILL   191
Illustrated by D. Alexandroff

Bridges Help Us Every Day   BY DAVID B. STEINMAN   197
Illustrated by George Bobritzky

Bridges   BY JAMES S. TIPPETT   205
Illustrated by Clare Bice

Clipper Ship   BY NANCY BYRD TURNER   206

A Magic Mineral   BY LILIAN HOLMES STRACK   207
Illustrated by Ernest Crichlow

The Rock That Glowed in the Dark

BY LILIAN HOLMES STRACK 214
Illustrated by Eleanor Mill

Atoms Are Like Letters BY JEROME S. MEYER 220
Illustrated by Charles Clement

New Light for the World BY G. GLENWOOD CLARK 225
Illustrated by Seymour Fleishman

Ben Franklin of Old Philadelphia

BY MARGARET COUSINS 234
Illustrated by Fritz Eichenberg

Mr. Bell Invents the Telephone

BY KATHERINE B. SHIPPEN 237
Illustrated by Serge Hollerbach

Johann Gutenberg and His Type

BY SAM AND BERYL EPSTEIN 244
Illustrated by Ezra Jack Keats

John James Audubon

BY MARGARET AND JOHN KIERAN 247
Illustrated by Herbert Danska

John Muir Comes to America BY CHARLES NORMAN 255
Illustrated by Eleanor Mill

Plant Peanuts BY ANNE TERRY WHITE 263
Illustrated by Ernest Crichlow

A Daring Voyage BY RALPH NADING HILL 272
Illustrated by Howard Simon

Airplane in a Cow Pasture BY QUENTIN REYNOLDS 281
Illustrated by Jacob Landau

"Calling All Cars" BY JACK GOULD 289
Illustrated by Bette J. Davis

Round-Trip to the Moon BY JACK GOULD 295
Illustrated by Bette J. Davis

Jet Propulsion BY NELSON F. BEELER

AND FRANKLYN M. BRANLEY 301
Illustrated by Serge Hollerbach

XX

Chemistry Is Nature's Magic   BY JEROME S. MEYER   303
    Illustrated by Charles Clement
To See the Very Small   BY JULIUS SCHWARTZ   306
    Illustrated by Gil Miret

P.S. *In cases where these selections are excerpts from longer* 309
    books, refer to this for further reading opportunities.
SUBJECT INDEX   311
ILLUSTRATORS' INDEX   317
ALPHABETICAL INDEX OF AUTHORS AND TITLES   318

Man and
His World

Earth and Sky

The World
Stands Out
on Either Side

BY EDNA ST. VINCENT MILLAY

Illustrated by George Bobritzky

THE world stands out on either side
No wider than the heart is wide;
Above the world is stretched the sky,
No higher than the soul is high.

LAND is the solid part of the earth, but it isn't the same everywhere. If we take long trips in a car or on trains we'll see places where the land is high and places where it is low. We shall find rough, hilly land and land that is flat. We shall visit places where the land gets lots of rain and shall go to others that are dry almost every day in the year. If we like, we can mark each place on a map. It will show the different kinds of land that are found in the different parts of our big country.

Plains are level-looking land where we see barns and towns and smoke from engines that are miles and miles away. We call plains in the West the Great Plains because they are so large. Some parts of the great Western plains look flat. Other parts have ridges and hills, or low places where bushes and trees can grow. The Great Plains don't get much rain in summer, when the sun shines brightly and the wind blows almost every day. The plains become hot and very dry when the sun shines and the wind keeps blowing day after day after day.

Across Our Country

BY CARROLL LANE FENTON AND MILDRED ADAMS FENTON

Illustrated by George Bobritzky

The word "prairie" means a grassy place among trees. But big prairies in the central part of our country have thousands and thousands of grassy places, and thousands of groves of trees. Prairies are not so flat as most plains, and they aren't so dusty and windy. They have hills and low, rounded ridges; they have creeks that run past the hills and many rivers that

3

flow toward the ocean, which is miles and miles and miles away. Prairies also have farms with fields of grain—with white houses and sheds and big red barns and cattle that live in grassy pastures. It is fun to watch cattle and count the red barns while we ride across the prairies.

Deserts are found in the Western part of our country between long mountain ranges. Desert land is bare and dusty and dry, for it does not get much rain. When rain does fall, most of the water runs away. It runs away in rivers and foaming creeks that flow through narrow, steep-sided valleys or spread out over barren flats. When the rain stops, all these creeks and rivers dry up, and so do the flat places. Soon the deserts don't have any more water than they had before the storm.

Many deserts do not have trees, for trees cannot grow on such dry, dusty land. Other deserts have almost no plants at all because the ground is full of salt and other things that keep plants from growing. But most deserts are not so bare as that. They have a few small trees that live in low places where water stays deep down in the ground. They have bushes that grow in round green domes. They have prickly cactus plants that spread out or stand up straight, like green tree trunks that have spines instead of leaves. Such plants are able to live on the desert because they do not need much water and can stand the hot, dry summer days.

There are hills in many parts of our country—even on prairies, deserts and the plains. Hills are places where the land is high and rough, with ridges and steep slopes. Roads often wind in and out around the ridges or climb their sloping sides. Creeks and rivers wind in and out, too, but they never wind their way up slopes. Instead, they flow through low places called valleys that lie between the hills.

4

Many hills are close to other hills, just as people stand close to each other when they are in a crowd. But hills on the Great Plains are not crowded, and many of them stand out alone. These lone hills on the plains are often called buttes. So are other steep, lone hills in the middle of big, flat-bottomed valleys. "Butte" (beut) is a French word for "steep hill." It was used long, long ago by men who came from the French part of Canada. These men climbed buttes to look across wide valleys. They watched for lone hills that showed where to go as they traveled across the plains.

The word "mesa" (may′ sa) is Spanish. It means "table," and mesas are table-shaped hills. They have steep, bare-looking sides and level tops that are made of solid stone. A few mesas stand all alone, like buttes, in the middle of wide, grassy plains. But most mesas are found on dry, brown deserts, or in valleys among mountains and high, level places that are known as table-lands, or plateaus. When you see one of these table-lands you may think that it looks like a big mesa with steep, bare sides and a level top that is covered with strong, hard stone.

Badlands in the West got their name because they were bad, bad country to cross in the days when there were no roads. Most badlands look almost like deserts with many valleys and steep, bare hills that are made of clay or sandstone. Some valleys are wide and others are narrow. Some hills are long, pointed ridges and others are small mesas or buttes. When the sun shines, the badlands become hot and dry. When

rain falls, water runs down the hillsides and covers the bare bottoms of valleys with soft, sticky mud.

Many dark-colored, stony plains in the West were made when melted rock called lava (lah′ va) came out of cracks in the ground. At first the lava was hot and soft and runny. It was so soft that it spread out over flat places. It was so runny that it flowed into valleys until they were full. While the lava was flowing and spreading it cooled and turned into hard, solid stone. It made buttes where the lava piled up high. It made ridges and hollows and queer twisty lumps that were formed where the lava rolled along before it became solid.

Some mountains look like great big hills that have grassy slopes and groves of trees all the way to their tops. Many people live among these mountains. They have farms or ranches in the valleys, where they grow crops of hay or sugar beets or corn. Sometimes they grow crops on the mountain slopes, too —crops of grapes and peaches and apples and prunes which are sold to people who live in cities where there isn't enough room to grow things. When you ride among tree-covered mountains like these look for farms or hay ranches in the valleys; look for orchards or fruit ranches upon the mountain slopes.

Other mountains are steep and very high. They have rocky slopes and cliffs like stone walls. They have ridges and pointed tops, or peaks, that are covered with snow and ice. The valleys between these high mountains are narrow and very, very deep. Many valleys have blue lakes at the bottom. The lakes are filled with water from melting snow banks or with rain water that runs down from ridges and peaks and cliffs. In summer time people come to these high, snowy mountains. They come to hike and ride and climb the peaks or to camp and fish and have good times beside the deep blue lakes.

6

I LOVE my prairies, they are mine
　　From zenith to horizon line,
Clipping a world of sky and sod
　　Like the bended arm and wrist of God.

I love their grasses. The skies
　　Are larger, and my restless eyes
Fasten on more of earth and air
　　Than seashore furnishes anywhere.

I love the hazel thickets, and the breeze,
　　The never resting
　　　　prairie winds. The trees
That stand like spear points high
　　Against the dark blue sky

My Prairies

BY HAMLIN GARLAND

Illustrated by Ernest Crichlow

Are wonderful to me.
　　I love the gold
Of newly shaven
　　stubble, rolled
A royal carpet toward the sun, fit to be
　　The pathway of a deity.

I love the life of pasture lands; the songs of birds
　　Are not more thrilling to me than the herd's
Mad bellowing or the shadow stride
　　Of mounted herdsmen at my side.

I love my prairies, they are mine
　　From high sun to horizon line.
The mountains and the cold gray sea
　　Are not for me, are not for me.

7

Fog

BY CARL SANDBURG

Illustrated by Gil Miret

THE fog comes
   on little cat feet.

It sits looking
over harbor and city
on silent haunches
and then moves on.

The Rivers and the Sea

AN AESOP FABLE

Illustrated by Gil Miret

ONCE upon a time all the Rivers combined to protest against the action of the Sea in making their waters salt. "When we come to you," said they to the Sea, "we are sweet and drinkable; but when once we have mingled with you, our waters become as briny and unpalatable as your own." The Sea replied shortly, "Keep away from me and you'll remain sweet."

9

"**S**HIP in distress, sir!" called the lookout to the officer on the bridge of the cruiser. The officer scanned the distant vessel through his glass for some moments, while the cruiser drove on through the still sea. The distance was still too great for him to read the flags of the International Code which were hanging limply from the yard of the distant ship. But every beat of the engines brought them closer.

"Can't make them out, sir," said a junior officer, who had also been observing the sailing craft through his glass. "Shall I signal?"

The officer nodded and a quiet order was given. A moment later a sailor on the signal bridge began to wave a small flag in each hand. Up, down, right, left—letter by letter he spelled out a message to the captain of the distressed ship. Again he repeated the message, and then again, slower this time.

The Ocean and Its Work

BY RUDOLPH BRETZ

Illustrated by Ezra Jack Keats

"Can't read signal," he was saying. "Wigwag! Can't read signal. Wigwag!"

"They're answering," he reported.

On the foretopmast crosstree of the ship, the officer's glass picked out a figure, clinging with one hand to the shrouds. In the other hand he held a flag, which he swung in answer to the message of the cruiser. Up, down, left, right—slowly he spelled out his message, as the officers on the cruiser, more than two miles away, read it letter by letter.

10

"Water! Water! Water!" the distressed ship was signaling, over and over again.

"Probably they have been becalmed for days," commented the junior officer. "Hasn't been a breath of air for more than a week."

The other officer laughed. He gave a message to the signaller which caused the men on the bridge to look at him in astonishment.

"Dip it out of the sea—Dip it out of the sea," signaled the wigwag.

By this time the cruiser was much closer to the slowly drifting ship. There was no answer from it. Perhaps they thought the reply was a cruel joke.

Now the course of the cruiser was altered a little, and in a few moments it would be close enough to hail the ship. The officer continued to chuckle to himself. The junior officer could not believe he would ignore the request for help and so violate that unwritten law of the sea which all ships observe.

At last they were within hailing distance. The officer seized his megaphone.

"Dip it out of the sea," he shouted. "You're off the mouth of the Amazon."

There was no land in sight. Every man on the bridge of the cruiser knew that the mainland of South America lay more than fifty miles to the west, but every one of them joined in the laugh. The sailing vessel probably had been floating in fresh water for at least a day.

The great Amazon River of Brazil pours its tremendous stream of water into the sea in such great volume that it is still fresh more than a hundred miles out to sea. At the same time the river water also carries with it the mud and minerals which the river has swept from far inland. Let us see what happens to the material which rivers carry to the sea.

Suppose we put on diving suits and walk on the bottom of the ocean. We are close inshore when our helmets are fastened on and we wave a good-bye to the men who are manning the air pumps. We will climb down the short ladder of our tender, the boat which accompanies us and furnishes air for our diving suits.

Our feet soon touch bottom and we begin our long walk out to sea, down a gently sloping plain. Our heavy shoes, weighted with lead, are very necessary now. Although we could hardly move in them when on deck, now they keep us from floating up to the surface.

The going is very rough at first. The bottom seems to be made of rounded pebbles, worn quite smooth by the action of the waves breaking on the shore. There are larger stones, covered with oysters and black mussels, and sea anemones with

12

their many tiny arms waving in the water.

Soon we find the bottom changing to sand. Here is a large red starfish creeping slowly over the bottom. Here is a tall mass of green seaweed stretching up toward the greenish light above which we know is the surface. As we look we can see our air hose, a dark line, and a string of bubbles going up, up, toward the dark shadow which is our tender. It is slowly moving seaward to keep pace with us.

The sand bottom continues for miles, so we come to the top and the boat takes us farther from shore. We descend again, this time so deep we must use our electric searchlights. The light attracts fishes and we are annoyed by darting dark shapes rushing at us. They are easily frightened though, and all we have to do is to insert a finger in the elastic cuff at the wrists of our suits. A swift stream of silvery "bullets" of air shoots out as from a machine gun, and the curious fish leave us in peace.

Finally the sand becomes finer grained. The reason for this is that even in the stormiest weather, the heavier grains are not washed out so far. After a long stretch of this fine sand we discover that the bottom is changing again. Now it is a soft clay that feels like mud under our feet. Our leaden shoes sink deeper and deeper into it, and walking becomes difficult. There is little life on the bottom now.

Suddenly we see a large flat shape move like a shadow on the mud. We turn our torches on it and see a great gray halibut flat against the bottom. This fish lives its whole life swimming on its side, and both eyes look out from the same side of the head. Without waiting to see what manner of intruders we are, the huge fish turns and vanishes in a swirling cloud of mud.

We know that this clay will extend for many miles more, because it is made out of the fine mud the rivers carry down to the sea. It is soft because it is so fine. When mud is fine it takes a long time to settle in water and to make the soft clay in which we stand. The waves stir up the water, so the mud is carried miles from the shore.

We signal our tender to pull us up, and very slowly we are hauled to the surface. It takes a long time, because if the men pulled us up very fast the sudden change in the pressure would give us the "bends," a painful trouble that divers sometimes have.

When our helmets are unscrewed we find that we are out of sight of land. The sun is so bright, and in such contrast to the murky deeps from which we have come, that we blink our eyes. Now the tender starts full speed for the open sea. We are going to find out what the ocean bottom is like a hundred miles from shore.

The water there is too deep for us to use diving suits, but it is still very shallow compared to the rest of the ocean. Instead of going down ourselves, we drop a "bottom-sampler" on the end of a long, heavy line. The sampler is like a large clam shell. Its two halves are wide open, but when it strikes the bottom a strong spring snaps it shut. The two halves dig into the bottom and a piece of the ocean bed is firmly held between them.

Our sampler drops out of sight and the line is paid out. Finally it stops running. We wait a moment and then pull it in, hand over hand. The "clam shell" comes up, dripping.

We pry the halves apart and find a mass of soft gray mud. This is called ooze. It is made up of the shells of thousands upon thousands of tiny plants and animals which live in the water. Sometimes these forms of life are called plankton. The sea is full of them, most of them living near the surface. Millions and millions of them live, multiply and (after a short life) die. Their dead bodies are continually settling to the bottom to form this ooze.

As this layer becomes thicker, and as other sediments are deposited on top, its weight and the weight of the other layers and that of the water, press down with enormous force and turn the layers of ooze into rock. The shells of the tiny animals were made of lime, and the rock that is made is what we call limestone.

Limestone is not the only rock the ocean makes. The gravelly bottom which we first saw will solidify into rock, too. It will then be called *conglomerate*, a word which means "rolled together." But we have an even better name for this mixture of pebbles and different kinds of rock. We call it "pudding stone."

The sand we walked over for so many miles will also turn into rock if enough layers of sand and mud are deposited on

top of it to squeeze it down and press it heavily enough. Tiny plankton also live in the shallow water, and the lime from their shells acts as a cement to hold the closely packed sand grains together. The rock so made is called sandstone. This is the same kind of rock that is often found when workmen blast out a railroad cut.

Even the mud we had so much trouble walking through will, in time, become a kind of rock. It settles together, the particles closer and closer, and becomes more and more tightly packed. Finally it hardens into shale. The word means shell, but it does not refer to sea shells but to the fact that the rock lies in shell-like flakes or layers. The slate of which blackboards are made was originally shale. So was the slate which is split into thin slabs and used like shingles on roofs.

These are not the only rocks made in the ocean. Have you ever seen a piece of coral? This is a rock-like deposit that the coral animal builds. The coral animal can live only in the sea, under water. It makes lime and builds itself a kind of house for protection. Millions of them live together and build up these stony deposits. Although each coral animal lives but a short time, other corals growing nearby keep adding to the deposit. The live coral builds its house on top of the dead coral's house. Others do the same, and thus the coral rock grows and grows.

In the tropical seas there are a great many islands which have been built by corals. They are not far out of the water generally, but the living corals keep adding to them year by year. Some of the islands south of Florida are made entirely of the lime from corals.

You can see, then, that rocks are being made in the ocean all the time. Perhaps the same water which carried the worn soil and minerals into the sea is helping, by its weight, to transform particles of rock into a new kind of rock.

ALL hills and mountains are not made by wrinkles in the ground. Mountains which spout fire and steam up into the air are made very differently.

These are terrible mountains although they are sometimes very beautiful. They are called volcanoes. We have only one active volcano in the United States. It is in California, and is called Mount Lassen. However, there are a lot of magnificent volcanoes in Alaska.

There have always been these fire-shooting mountains on the earth, and very long ago probably there were more than there are now. Most of these old volcanoes have stopped throwing up great columns of fire, steam, and red-hot rock. It is perfectly safe now to climb up one and look down into the hole, which was once full of white-hot melted rock.

In some volcanoes there is so much hot melted rock that it rises up to the top of the hole and actually overflows. Then it runs down the sides of the mountain.

Streams of melted rock are

Volcanoes

and

Earthquakes

BY
W. MAXWELL REED

Illustrated by Kurt Wiese

called lava and the hole in the top of the volcano from which the lava comes is called the crater.

There are two kinds of volcanoes. One kind is high with steep sides and the top is sometimes snow-capped. The sides are fairly steep because they are made mostly of ashes, which are so rough and cling to each other so well that they don't roll down over the land as the lava does.

The other kind of volcano is not so high but is very large

18

at the base. The sides have a gentle slope, because they are mostly made of frozen lava. Unlike the ashes, lava will flow. So this kind of a volcano is usually not so high and has long, gently sloping sides.

When the lava is flowing down the side of the mountain, it is very dangerous to climb to the top. It is even dangerous to be anywhere near the foot of the mountain, because the hot lava keeps on flowing and sometimes spreads out over the country.

It is hard to imagine what a terrible time people have if they live near a mountain that is pouring hot melted rock all over the country.

Sometimes a whole forest will be crushed, burnt, and buried by this fearful flood of melted rock. Nothing can stop it. Even if you built a strong stone wall in front of it, you couldn't keep it from flowing right along across the country.

It would just push the stones to one side and bury them in the hot lava.

Thousands of houses have been destroyed by streams of lava. You may think it strange that people should build their homes near a volcano. No one ever thinks of building a house in the bed of a stream which comes down from a mountain. In the summer when there is almost no water in the brooks and streams it would be possible to build a house there. But everyone knows that when spring comes, a torrent of foaming water would crush and carry away any house that anyone had been foolish enough to build.

Strange as it may seem, people do build houses not only near the foot of a volcano but actually on the side. They say: "It has been so many years since any lava came out of the crater and flowed down the mountain, that we think it is perfectly safe to build our house on the slope of the volcano."

Near the foot of a volcano the slope is usually very gradual. It is much like the sides of hills in your town. You have probably seen many houses built on the side of a hill.

The most important reason why people like to live near the foot of a volcano is because the rich earth there makes such good gardens. Many things grow better there than in the soil miles away in open country.

Sometimes families have lived so long on the side of a volcano that they have almost forgotten that any melted rock ever came flowing down. Then one day they hear a rumbling noise down in the earth. It sounds as if guns were being fired in a cave far down in the mountain. Every day these sounds grow louder and they come more often.

Then the ground begins to tremble. The pictures on the wall begin to swing back and forth. A plate may fall off a shelf and break. Those who come back from climbing to the top of

20

the volcano will tell the people living on the slope that the terrible lava is rising in the crater and that soon it may overflow and come rushing down the side of the mountain.

Then the people, if they are wise, pack up their things and get as far from the volcano as possible. Sometimes a few foolish people think that there is no danger and stay on the side of the volcano. They are often killed when the lava comes rushing down.

The lava seems to come from far down in the earth. Something down there pushes it up toward the surface of the earth. If it can find a weak place it will crowd through and come out into the air. Then it flows all over the neighborhood until something under the earth stops pushing.

We don't know what starts the lava flowing; neither do we understand what stops it. All we know is that the crater of a volcano will sometimes have red-hot lava in it for many years. Then for hundreds of years a volcano will be as quiet and cold as any hill near your town.

When a volcano doesn't spout lava from its crater, it stops growing; but every time the melted rock comes out of the crater and flows down the sides, the mountain grows a little larger. That is because when the lava stops flowing it cools just wherever on the mountain it happens to be. When it cools it becomes rock.

When you see a picture of a very high volcano you will know that its crater has poured out ashes and lava many times. Every eruption of the volcano has made the mountain grow a little larger and higher.

Another thing happens to a volcano: if it doesn't grow larger it will surely grow smaller. Those little brooks that carry away our hills will also take particles of rock from the volcano and carry them down to the larger streams and then to the rivers.

After a while the brooks will take away the whole volcano, bit by bit. But of course, if fresh lava keeps coming from the crater and cooling into hard rock, the volcano will keep its size and won't grow smaller.

Some old volcanoes, that had no more lava to spill over their sides, have been so worn away by the brooks that they have almost disappeared.

A curious thing sometimes happens to a very old volcano. The lava in the crater cools and becomes solid rock. That usually means that the volcano is dead. The busy little brooks then continue their work of carrying away parts of the volcano, until after a very long time the whole mountain has disappeared except one part. The lava in the crater that cooled into hard rock is sometimes too hard for the brooks to wear away rapidly.

There it stands, hundreds of feet high, a great column of hard rock. So the crater has changed from a hole in the top of a mountain to a great column of rock that can be seen from far over the land.

We realize that a big oak tree can grow from a little acorn which is planted in the ground. We know that after hundreds of years the tree falls down and becomes a part of the ground. Now we know that a huge volcano can grow and then gradually disappear. But, instead of hundreds of years, the life of a volcano is millions of years.

You remember that before the volcano spouted lava and ashes from its crater and sent a volume of steam and fire high into the air, the people living near the foot of the mountain heard noises that seemed to come from the earth. Then the ground shook and china on the pantry shelves was broken.

When the ground shakes like that we call it an earthquake. Once in a great while every place in the world has an earthquake. In most places the ground trembles such a tiny amount that we hardly feel it. When such a little earthquake comes at night most of us sleep through it and never know that it has happened.

In some parts of the world the earthquakes are terrible. The ground will shake so much that houses fall down. If the earthquake is near the ocean great waves roll upon the land. These waves are sometimes higher than a house. Big ocean steamers have been known to have been carried far up on the land by earthquake waves. When the ocean became quiet once more, there the steamer would be, high and dry, and no water anywhere near it.

The ground can shake without the help of a volcano.

We have learned that land can wrinkle and form hills and mountains. In some parts of the world these wrinkles may still be rising, but so slowly that no one is sure just what is happening.

The surface of our earth resembles the ice on a river. The blocks of ice are always cracking and moving a trifle even though the river continues to be frozen solid. When a slight movement takes place in the river ice, loud noises are heard. If you were skating on that ice you would feel it tremble.

Some earthquakes are caused in much the same way as the movements of ice on the river. If the surface of the earth is wrinkling, even very slowly, it is natural for the land near the wrinkle to shake.

There are so many kinds of earthquakes that we will talk only about those that are made by a volcano.

There must be a quantity of melted rock far down in the earth, because so much lava comes up through the craters of volcanoes. Millions of years ago thousands of square miles of this country were covered with enormous masses of hot lava.

Huge volcanoes were pouring lava all over the northwestern part of the United States.

When the lava is forced up through the crater with great force, large rocks are thrown high in the air. They make it dangerous for anyone to come near a volcano when it is behaving in this way. Also, columns of steam and something that looks like smoke come out of the crater and float off as clouds.

That dark, smoky-looking cloud is really very finely ground-up rock. It is ground up as fine as powder and stays up in the air the way smoke does. After the wind has carried it away for long distances, these tiny particles of rock fall to the ground.

If there are many big volcanoes which keep throwing out these smoky-looking clouds, the ground will be covered with fine powder.

Sometimes butterflies and other insects are buried in this powder; then millions of years afterward people dig them up and find that they have been beautifully kept during all those many years. We can then see what the ancient butterflies looked like.

Of course in all that time the powder has changed to stone. Now if you want to find one of these very old butterflies, you must crack open many flat stones. You must go to some place where the powdered rock once fell and if you are lucky you will find a butterfly all turned to stone.

Once in a great while a volcano will explode. This will happen if something down in the earth tries to push up more lava and steam than the crater can hold. If the old lava in the crater has become cold and hard, the pressure from the new lava may be more than the volcano can stand.

Once upon a time a mountain with a crater exploded near

Java, in the Indian Ocean. Its name was Krakatoa. This was a gigantic explosion.

Since Krakatoa was entirely surrounded by water, some tremendous waves were made when it exploded. It was said that the largest wave was as high as a ten story building. For hundreds of miles along the shore not only were beaches covered with water, but towns and even cities were flooded. When the waves had gone over the land as far as they could, they ran back to the ocean. Many of you have seen small waves on the beach or on the edge of a pond do exactly the same thing. A small wave will roll up on the sand and then the water will rush back and carry small pebbles with it. When the water of this giant wave rushed back to the Indian Ocean, it carried houses and people with it.

The noise of the explosion was so great that it was heard in Australia, which is 1,900 miles from Krakatoa. If such an explosion had occurred in St. Louis, it might have been heard on both the Pacific and Atlantic coasts. Sound travels farther at sea because there are no mountains to interfere. The Rocky and Appalachian Mountains would make it more difficult for the sound of an explosion in St. Louis to reach the ocean on both sides of the United States.

The Krakatoa explosion was in the days before the invention of radio. When these noises were heard people didn't know what caused them. It never occurred to them that a volcano had exploded. In some seaports they thought that a ship far out in the ocean was sinking and was firing a cannon to let other ships know that it needed help. Two steamers went out from one harbor to hunt for this imaginary boat and rescue its crew.

The land near the volcano shook and powdered rock was sent up into the sky beyond the highest clouds. Only a mere rim of the great volcano was left. The whole mountain had been blown up into the sky.

Fortunately most volcanoes give warning by rumbling when there is going to be an eruption of fire and melted rock. It is only once in a very great while that a volcano blows off its top and causes a great earthquake.

JUST imagine yourself climbing the "Highway to the Stars"—the beautiful ribbon-road to Palomar. It is the scattered range of the San Jacinto Mountains about fifty miles north of San Diego and one hundred miles southeast of Los Angeles. The mountain the road ascends rises some 6,000 feet in the air and is capped by a single flat block of granite about thirty miles long and ten wide. Upon this has been built Palomar Observatory.

At Palomar there is a million pounds of glass and steel working with a precision the most expensive watch could never imitate. It is the giant "eye" of the 200-inch telescope.

Giant "Eyes"

BY CATHERINE
E. BARRY

Illustrated by Mauro Caputo

The gigantic telescope is higher than a fifteen story building. Its mirror is ten thousand times more powerful as a gatherer of light than the tiny lens Galileo used when he discovered the moons of Jupiter in 1610. It is more than a million times as keen as the human eye. It is the finest that science and engineering have created to date. Although it was one man's dream, it is made up of a thousand arts and inventions. To build such a telescope six million dollars was raised and its maintenance costs several million more.

Although equipped with powerful "eyes," the 200-inch telescope is not used as a viewer of stars; its purpose is photography. To receive a perfect image from it, all conditions surrounding the telescope must be completely controlled. There cannot be the slightest change in temperature; there can be no vibration, no air currents, and even sounds must be eliminated if perfect results are to be obtained.

On Palomar no privileges are allowed visitors; it is like an operating room of a hospital from which visitors are barred. They can view this towering giant only from a glass showcase at one side.

The giant "eyes" do not work alone. A "finder telescope" known as the Schmidt camera is used to explore the sky quickly in order to locate important new objects which the 200-inch telescope can analyze in detail. Without the Schmidt camera, the giant would be greatly handicapped. It can scan an area so limited it would take 27,000 photographs to cover the sky, a task that would require years of work. The Schmidt camera because of its type plates and mirrors can do the job in a single year.

The 200-inch telescope has now "touched" an object some two billion light years away. What would a 300-inch telescope accomplish? That remains to be seen.

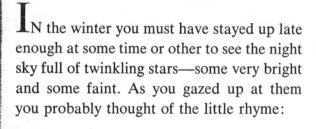

IN the winter you must have stayed up late enough at some time or other to see the night sky full of twinkling stars—some very bright and some faint. As you gazed up at them you probably thought of the little rhyme:

Twinkle, twinkle, little star;
How I wonder what you are,
Up above the world so high,
Like a diamond in the sky—

The Stars

BY JEROME S. MEYER

Illustrated by Emma Landau

and wondered just what those tiny little twinkling lights really are. Before learning about them you had better get ready for some big surprises and you will have to pay close attention because we are going to mention some very big numbers.

The sun is more than a million times as big as the earth. It would take you about three years to walk around the earth. If you could walk at the same speed on the sun it would take you more than 300 years to walk around it.

And now for your first surprise. The sun that we see in the sky every day is really a very small star. The stars that you see in the night sky are all great big suns and many of them are millions of times as big as our sun! Because they are all so many, many hundreds of billions of miles away, they look like tiny little lights in the night sky.

Now how many of these stars—let us call them "far away suns"—do you suppose there are in the sky and beyond the

30

sky? Do you think that you could count them all? Of course you couldn't. There are more than a hundred billion of them. There are so many, in fact, that if each star were as big as a drop of water and they all got together, there would be enough water to make a large lake! If you tried to count them and kept on counting and counting night and day as fast as you could, it would take you a few million years to count them all. And of course that is very silly because you could never live a few million years.

Now why don't we see all the stars? If there are so many in the sky why isn't the whole sky a solid roof of them all crowded together? We know that there is really much more black sky than there are stars. Why? The answer is that most of the stars are so very, very far away that no matter how big they are you cannot see them. You know that if you and your friend are on a long straight road and you run in one direction and he runs in the opposite direction, he will soon be so far away from you that he will look like a tiny speck. If the road is straight and long enough and you both keep on running there will be a time when you won't be able to see your friend at all—he will be out of sight! That is the way with the stars. Most of them are too far away to see even if they are thousands of times bigger than the sun. Some of them are so far away that when they get together they look like a thin light cloud in the night sky. This is called the "Milky Way" because it is very pale and white like milk. It looks to you and to me just like a cloud but it is really made up of billions of huge suns much larger than our sun.

No boy or girl in all the world and no grown-up either can possibly imagine how far away the stars are and how big it is out there beyond the sky. The space goes on and on and on forever—there just isn't any end to it at all.

31

The stars are always shining—they never stop. They shine in the daytime just as much as they do at night. We can't see them in the daytime because the sun is too bright and the sun is bright because it is so much nearer to us than any other star. The sun lights up the air and turns the black night sky into a beautiful blue and this bright blue hides all the stars. If we could go far away from the earth and up beyond the air, the sky would be black and we should see the stars and the sun all out together. Sometimes we don't see any stars at night because the clouds are in the way. But an airplane pilot flying above the clouds will see the stars.

We know that the sun rises and sets every day. If stars are suns they must do the same thing—rise and set. And they do. A great many of the stars that we see at night rise in the east and set in the west, just like the sun. They all travel very slowly across the sky, just like the sun. Some stars rise late at night;

32

others rise very early in the evening. Still others rise in the daytime and you can't see them at all at that time of year. Stars are always rising and always setting every minute of the day and night. While you are reading this book stars are rising and setting even if the big sun prevents you from seeing them do so. If you were allowed to stay up all night and you could do it without falling asleep, and you watched the stars in the sky, you would see that they seem to move slowly from east to west.

One star that does not seem to move at all is Polaris, or the North Star. It is almost directly over the North Pole of the earth and if you could go up to the North Pole it would be right over your head and you would have to bend your head way back to look at it.

All the stars in the sky seem to move slowly. Of course we have already learned that the stars don't really move noticeably. We are moving with the earth, so we think that the stars move.

Have you ever heard of the Great Dipper? If you haven't I'll tell you about it now. It is made up of seven bright stars which form a huge cup with a handle on it. They look like a great dipper up there in the night sky. Ask mother or dad to show you the Great Dipper.

The North Star is one of the most important stars in the sky. Captains on ships that cross the ocean look at it and can tell where they are. Just think of that—if you were somewhere in the middle of the big ocean on a ship at night and all around you was nothing but inky black ocean and above you there was nothing but stars and stars, could you tell where you were? Of course you couldn't. But once you found the North Star you could tell right away how high it was in the sky and you would know right away how far you were from the North Pole.

You can see how easy it would be for ships to get lost on the ocean because the ocean is so big. But as long as they have stars like the North Star to guide them they will never get lost.

In the night sky we find all kinds of stars. There are big stars and little stars; bright stars and dim stars; double stars and single stars. There are all kinds of stars in the sky. And don't forget that among these stars there are our friends, the planets—Mercury, Venus, Mars, Jupiter, Saturn and the rest. They all shine at night just like the stars, and they look just like the stars—but we know that they are not. They shine because the sun lights them up just the way it lights up the moon. They have no light of their own and if the sun went out they would all go out too. They would be there just the same, but they would be dark.

The brightest of all the planets and the brightest light in the night sky when the moon is not shining is Venus. It may be seen over in the western sky just after the sun sets. It is a truly beautiful sight—you should see it before you go to bed each night. Some people call it the "evening star" when it is out in the early evening, and a "morning star" when it rises in the morning before the sun.

Now, I'll tell you about one of the biggest stars. It is called Alpha Herculis and it is about seventy-five million times as far away from us as the sun is! You remember that the sun is more than ninety million miles away? Well, this giant star is more than fifty million times ninety million miles away! If you could travel in the fastest airplane ever built from here to Alpha Herculis, and you kept on going night and day, night and day without ever stopping, it would take you more than a thousand million years to get to this star, and when you got there you would weigh more than any mountain in the world.

The great giant star Alpha Herculis is more than five hundred million times as big as our sun and it is about a billion times as big as the earth! It is so big that in one gulp it could swallow up the sun and four of the planets as they go around the sun, and have plenty of room to spare. Yet it is so far away that it appears to be no bigger than a dot of light in the sky.

Most of the stars, like the sun, are brilliant hot exploding gases and are not solid at all. But some stars are very solid and heavy, hundreds of times heavier and more solid than our earth. If you dig in your garden and lift a little shovel full of earth you have no trouble lifting it. It might weigh a few

pounds. If you were on some of the distant stars that are solid and not gases and you tried to lift the same little shovel full of star dust you would find that it weighed thousands and thousands of pounds. A handful of dust brought to the earth would be far too heavy, not only to lift, but to put on anything. If you put it on a table it would smash the table; if you put it on the floor it would crash through the floor—for a chunk of star, no bigger than a small stone, would weigh much more than an automobile, and a piece the size of an ordinary brick would weigh as much as a big locomotive engine!

Now here is still another surprise for you. You know how fast you can run and how slow this is when you compare it with an automobile. And an automobile is slow when you compare it to an airplane and an airplane is slow when you compare it to a bullet. But the fastest thing in the world is light. A beam of light travels so fast that if you could ride on it you would be able to go all around the world eight times before you could say "Mississippi." Light travels a million miles in about five seconds! Just try to think how far it would travel in a day and then try to imagine how far it would travel in a year. At this speed it travels about six million, million miles in a year. So far away are some of the stars that it takes their light hundreds and thousands of years to get here. If you were on one of these distant stars and could look back on the earth you would see the light that started hundreds of years ago from the earth. You would not see the world as it is now; you would see it as it was when Columbus discovered America. You would see the Indians roaming about North America and many other things that happened hundreds of years ago.

Now let's go out tonight and look up at the sky and be glad that we don't have to take a trip to any of the stars but can stay here on earth where we belong.

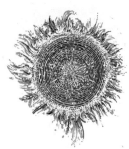

WE are used to thinking of our earth with its mighty oceans and vast continents as a pretty big globe—7,900 miles through the center, 25,000 miles around the equator. How big is it compared with the sun? A quarter as big? A tenth?

The earth is insignificant in comparison. You could pack 1,300,000 earths into the sun.

But figures of such size are hard to imagine. Suppose we could shrink the sun and the earth to a thousand-millionth of their size. Then the sun would become a ball five feet in diameter. The earth would be the size of a very small marble. It would be spinning 450 feet away— where we could just barely make it out.

That's how big the sun is. That's how small the earth is. And we, little people who make our home on a tiny marble, are completely dependent on the five-foot ball that keeps us forever prisoner circling around it.

Portrait

of the Sun

BY ANNE TERRY WHITE

Illustrated by Marvin Bileck

For the sun is the big astronomical fact in our lives. It is the sun that gives us light. It is the sun that gives us heat. By causing evaporation, the sun makes the rain come down. By heating land and water unequally, it causes the winds to blow. The sun makes food for the plants and they, in turn, feed the animals and us. And the sun gives us the base of power. For wood and coal and petroleum and falling water are all of the sun's making.

What a terrific amount of heat and light the sun pours

37

forth to accomplish all this! And yet the amount the earth catches is just a tiny fraction of the sun's radiation of heat in all directions. The heat of the sun is so great that the hottest fire is cold in comparison. At the surface the sun's heat measures 11,000° Fahrenheit. Nothing can be made that hot on earth for more than a fraction of a second. And still, inside the sun the temperature is much higher. It measures 29 million degrees Fahrenheit.

Every second the sun pours out into space over four million tons of energy. And "tons" is not just a figure of speech as we use it here. For even the light from an electric bulb has a little weight, though too little to measure, and sunlight really is measured in tons. Of those millions of tons the earth gets four pounds a second. The pounds add up to 173 tons a day. That may not sound like much after all the big figures we have been quoting. But if we had to pay for the light and heat we get from the sun for nothing, it would cost us $1,700,000,000,000 an hour. And that is too big a figure for most of us to read, let alone understand.

But what keeps the sun going? We know that a fire dies if it isn't fed. We know that we ourselves waste away if we don't eat. If the sun isn't getting anything from outside and is losing four million tons of energy a second, why doesn't it grow cold?

The answer is: it will in time. The sun is indeed using up its own substance to make its radiant heat. But the sun is so big and is using its substance so sparingly that the danger of its growing cold is very remote—and so infinitely far off in time that nobody need bother his head about it. The sun is extremely economical. It is using up only one million-millionth (1/1,000,000,000,000) of its resources a year. So, although the sun has been shining for several thousand million years, it is still extremely hot. It is so glowing hot that at the distance

38

of 93 million miles it dazzles our eyes. We cannot bear to look at it.

What, then, is the sun made of? Surely nothing so hot as the sun can remain a solid!

Surely not. The sun is a tremendous globe of glowing gas. On earth all the gases we know are much, much lighter than any liquid. On the sun, however, the gas particles are packed so tightly that on the average they are heavier than water. And they are never at rest. They are tumbling and flaring and spurting like geysers. To the naked eye, the face of the sun appears as a near-disk with clean-cut edges. But that's because it is so bright that we cannot see its features clearly.

We used to have to wait till a total eclipse came along to see these great fountains of gas flaring out at the edges. Then we would realize what commotion there is on the sun. Now, through a special eclipse-making telescope, we can see the sun's plumes any time. We can sometimes see fountains of glowing gas shooting out hundreds of thousands of miles. And beyond that we can see the mysterious, silvery halo of the corona, the sun's outer atmosphere, which is not like our atmosphere at all. It is very hot and very thin and contains vapors of iron and nickel and calcium. At times of total eclipse it can be traced out to several million miles beyond the sun.

Tumbling and shooting out and falling back in, the restless gases that make up the sun are at the same time rotating continually. For, like the earth, the sun is always turning, though very, very slowly. How can we tell that? By watching the spots on the sun's surface. The sunspots don't stand still. They move all in one direction.

It may be a disappointment to you to hear that the sun is not perfect, and it was certainly a shock to the world when the great Italian astronomer, Galileo, pointed it out. But there are certainly dark spots on the sun, and once in a great while, even with the naked eye, you can see them, provided you look through a piece of smoked glass to cut down the glare. They are pretty big, too. They have to be more than a thousand

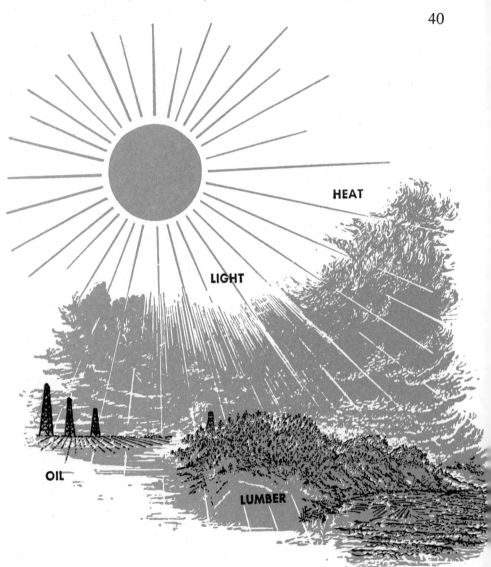

HEAT

LIGHT

OIL

LUMBER

The sun provides heat and light and causes the winds to blow.

miles across to be seen at all. But sometimes they are very much bigger. In 1947 there was one that had an area of five thousand million square miles. More than a hundred earths could have been swallowed up in it.

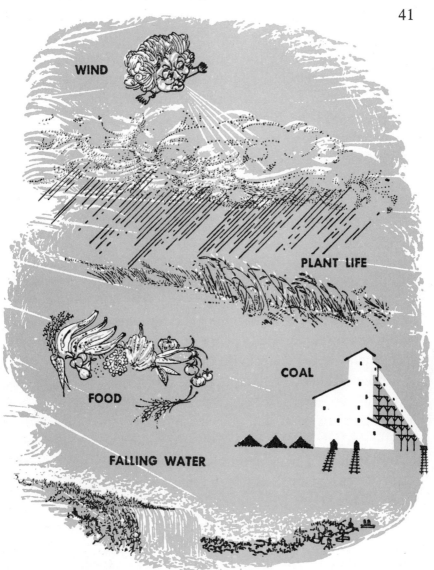

Wood, coal and petroleum are all of the sun's making.

Usually you see the sunspots in groups, and when one is visible all by itself you can be pretty sure it's the last of a lot that have disappeared. For sunspots break out in a group here, a group there. First they get bigger. Then, after a week or so, generally they die away. But as you watch them moving along day after day, it becomes clear that the sun turns, though not just like the earth; for the spots near the middle move faster than the ones higher up and lower down. And this, of course, is sure proof that the sun is not solid. If it were, the whole surface would have to move together.

What are these mysterious spots that come and go and rotate with the surface of the sun?

We don't know exactly. But we do know they are something like storms on earth. The gases in the sunspots swirl up and down. The way they act reminds you of tornadoes except that on the sunspots there is little circular twisting.

As for the number you can see at any one time, that differs with the year. In a poor year you might see fifty groups of spots; in an active year you might see 300 or 400 groups. But here is the curious thing. Sunspots go through a sort of cycle. About every eleven years there comes a big sunspot year. Then there are fewer again till the next big year.

From all this coming and going of sunspots one thing is sure. The sun, which to us appears so peaceful and tranquil as it rises and sets, is actually the scene of constant violence. In addition to the constant boiling up of light and heat from down below, there is a big-scale, longer rhythm in the sun. About every eleven years comes a high point and the spot break-outs repeat themselves. Only in each cycle the pattern of spots changes—they appear in different places on the sun.

Naturally, what we want to know is how all this affects us. The sun rules us so completely that it seems any change on the

42

sun should make a difference to us. Is it colder when the sun-spots are many and warmer when they are few?

Strangely enough, the answer is "no." Sunspots have no direct effect on our weather. But they do have an influence on earth. Often when a large group is passing the sun, the earth has a magnetic storm. We have trouble with our radios. And the northern lights are especially brilliant.

Such is the portrait of the sun. It seems very different from our own cool, solid, gentle earth with its grass and trees and clouds. And yet the materials of which earth and sun are made are the same. Oxygen, nitrogen, carbon, iron, sulphur, sodium, etc.—all the elements we know on earth—are present in the sun. There is an important difference however. These elements are not there in the same proportions. Only two are found in quantity on the sun—the two lightest, hydrogen and helium.

Indeed the sun is practically all hydrogen and helium. As someone has put it, of the other elements there isn't much more than "a smell." And that is just as it should be so far as we on earth are concerned. The secret of the sun's power lies in hydrogen and helium. It is by changing hydrogen into helium that the sun keeps going. Every time it converts four atoms of hydrogen into one atom of helium, the sun gets a little more energy. Heat and light are produced. It is just as though hydrogen were "fuel" which the sun is "burning," and helium the "ashes" that are left. Some of the other elements seem to be needed to keep the process going. But they aren't used up. Only the hydrogen grows less and less.

But that need alarm no one. We know the sun has been shining just as now for hundreds of millions of years at least, because there has been life on earth that long. And still the sun is mostly hydrogen. Have no fear! The sun will keep on shining for thousands of millions of years to come.

Silver

BY WALTER DE LA MARE

Illustrated by Mozelle Thompson

SLOWLY, silently, now the moon
Walks the night in her silver shoon;
This way and that, she peers, and sees
Silver fruit upon silver trees;
One by one the casements catch
Her beams beneath the silvery thatch;
Couched in his kennel, like a log,
With paws of silver sleeps the dog;
From their shadowy cote the white breasts peep
Of doves in a silver-feathered sleep;
A harvest mouse goes scampering by,
With silver claws, and a silver eye;
And moveless fish in the water gleam,
By silver reeds in a silver stream.

44

The Moon and Her Mother

AN AESOP FABLE

Illustrated by Mozelle Thompson

THE Moon once begged her
Mother to make her a gown.
"How can I?" replied she;
"there's no fitting your figure.
At one time you're a New
Moon, and at another you're
a Full Moon; and between
whiles you're neither
one nor the other."

45

HOW about a short trip to the Moon? No, this isn't an advertisement for a heavenly travel agency, for we really can't book passage on rocket ships for a voyage to our next-door neighbor in the skies.

But why worry about not having scientific transportation? We *do* have scientific information about what things are like on the Moon, and we have the most marvelous of all traveling methods right in our minds.

Let's imagine that we're on the Moon.

Oh! Here we are—on the Moon! It didn't take long, did it? Just like that! By imagining, we were able to jump from our Earth, about 250,000 miles to the Moon. Let's put on our imaginary air masks.

What's that? Can't you hear me? I'm yelling at the top of my lungs—can't you hear me? What do you say? I can't hear you. Why, I can't hear myself! Oh, I forgot to turn on the telephone. There! Now we can hear each

Let's Go to the Moon

BY ARMAND SPITZ

Illustrated by Jack Coggins

other. You see, there's no air on the Moon. That's the reason we brought air masks and air tanks on our imaginary trip. If we didn't have them, we couldn't breathe. And, since sound has to travel through air, on the Moon there simply isn't any sound. It's a good thing we put telephones inside these masks— otherwise we couldn't even hear each other. What's that?

Yes, it *is* terribly hot, isn't it? The Sun is shining down on the Moon. Without any air to absorb any of the sun's rays, all the heat is beating right down on top of us—that's what

46

makes it so much hotter than the hottest summer day. There's not even a breeze, for breezes are air in motion, and there is no air to move.

Sunset? Oh, no, the Sun won't set in a few hours. In fact, it won't set for about 250 hours. Oh, that's not surprising, no matter how strange it may sound. You see, every day on the Moon lasts about four of our Earth weeks. There are two weeks of daylight and two weeks of night.

During the two weeks of the Moon's daytime, the Sun shines brilliantly without ever stopping. There are never any clouds, never any fog or mist, never any rain. There's no water on the Moon, either, because it simply can't exist. If we were to spill some of this water from our special bottles it would disappear immediately—just evaporate into nothingness. During the two weeks of sunshine on the Moon, it gets a whole lot hotter here than it ever does at home on Earth.

Here's a great big rock. Let's get into the shade of that so we can cool off. Here we are. B-r-r-r! This isn't *cool*—it's *cold!* and isn't it dark? That's another thing. When there is no air, the shade gets completely dark, and it's terribly cold, too. On Earth the air gets warm and it also helps to scatter the light into shady places, but on the Moon when you're in the shade

it's really *dark,* and oh, so *cold!* If you stick your hand out in the Sun it will be hot, while the rest of you is almost freezing. If we were here during the two-week-long night, we'd all be frozen solid.

It's too cold here in the shade. The heat is bad, but it's better than this cold. Let's hop out there in the sunlight. Wait for me—don't jump so hard. Isn't it queer how far and how high you can jump without exerting your strength?

You could almost jump over a tree or a house, if there were trees or houses on the Moon. That's because the Moon is so much smaller than the Earth that everything weighs only one-sixth as much as it does on the Earth. A boy or girl who weighs ninety pounds at home would weigh only fifteen pounds here on the Moon. It wouldn't be any job at all to leap from one side of a wide street to the other.

I wish we had brought a baseball and bat. What a place the Moon would be to play baseball! You could bat a ball just as hard as you do on the Earth, but it would behave more like a rubber ball, staying up long enough so that every hit would probably be a home run. A good football player could make punts two or three times the length of an ordinary football field. A golf player would have to chase his drives for a half mile or more. If there was a circus on the Moon, we'd see the elephants jumping around as playfully as kittens. Even in walking we must be cautious in every step, otherwise we'd find ourselves constantly bouncing off the ground.

These things are all very interesting to experience, but look up there at the sky. The Sun is shining much more brilliantly than it has ever been known to shine on the Earth, and yet the whole sky is dark and filled with stars—more stars than we've

ever seen before. It's quite a queer feeling to see the brilliant Sun in the background of dense black, with all those untwinkling stars. Certainly nothing like that has ever been seen from Earth.

On the Earth, before the Sun rises in the morning or after it sets in the evening, its light still falls on the very fine bits of dust in the air, and they send their light on to us. This is what is called twilight. In the morning twilight the stars fade, and in the evening twilight the stars begin to come out. When the Sun is up, above the horizon, the entire atmosphere is made light, and none of the stars can be seen. Even if the Sun is hiding behind clouds in the daytime, the sky is still light. But, on the Moon, where there are no clouds, and where the Sun shines for two solid weeks, the skies are always dark and the stars are always out.

And then—look over there—see the crescent Earth? Oh, yes, that *is* the Earth. If you look carefully, you can see North and South America. It looks just the way the Moon looks from Earth, only much bigger and brighter, of course. But, just as the Moon changes its shape as we look at it from day to day, so the Earth changes its shape, too, as we look at it from the Moon. So there are crescent Earths and half Earths and full Earths, just as we are now used to seeing crescent Moons and half Moons and full Moons.

What we can see and feel on the Moon may sound fantastic, but scientists know positively that all of these things are true. The only thing lacking is actually going to the Moon to see them for ourselves. And, just as we were carried to the Moon by our imaginations, we put our imaginations to work in reverse to bring us down to Earth. After experiencing what we did on the Moon, we have every reason to say heartily, "There's no place like home."

50

Cloud Zoo

BY NORMA GILLETT

Illustrated by Mozelle Thompson

I THOUGHT I saw a cloud whale
Sail through a sea of blue;
It changed into an elephant
Of most unusual hue,
And even as I marvelled,
It split itself in two.

I watched a long white serpent
Winding its cloudy way,
To pounce upon a cloud frog
That unsuspecting lay.
The little frog became a bird
And slowly flew away.

All afternoon I watched them,—
Such magic as they knew!
I saw a white rhinoceros,
And white flamingos, too,
Till evening shut her deep blue tent
Over my private zoo.

51

The Storm

BY RICHARD AND
LOUIS UNTERMEYER

Illustrated by Susan Perl

THE other night before the storm
I sat and watched the rain-clouds swarm
Like great, black bees, so angry that
They buzzed with thunder. Well, I sat
And saw the wind come racing down,
Banging the shutters of the town;
Kicking the dust up in the road
And frightening every little toad.

He broke off branches for a toy,
Just like a large and wicked boy;
He threw the papers in the air,
And laughed as if he didn't care
What anyone might say or do.
He roared, and sang, and whistled, too.

Well, pretty soon things got so black
There was no sky except a crack,
One little streak of yellow light.
"See," father said, "just see how bright
The heavens shine behind it now;
And, look, it seems to spread somehow."

But father didn't understand
That I had seen it—seen God's hand
When, in a flash, so sharp and sly,
He tore a hole in that black sky.
I guess God must have missed my face
Behind the clouds in that dark place,
And so He made a hole to see
Whatever had become of me.

Then, when the space grew red and wide
And full of gold, and father cried,
"Was ever such a brilliant hue,"
I only smiled because I knew
I had been looking in God's eye.
Yet I kept still, till by and by,
When father cried, "The lightning, see!"
I had to laugh out loud with glee,
For it was God that winked at me.

LIGHTNING is the same thing as the light in an electric lamp. It is electricity. There is a very little bit of it in the light bulb, but in one flash of lightning there is twenty times as much electricity as all the people in the world use in a day and a night. Nature wastes a great deal of her electricity, because there may be a hundred flashes of it in a single storm, and there are nearly two thousand thunderstorms going on all over the world every minute of the day.

Benjamin Franklin, although very busy earning his living as a printer and serving his country in the cause of independence, found time to try to explain why so many strange things happened in the world every day. He wanted to know if the electricity that he made with a cell in his workshop was the same thing as the lightning that he saw in the sky during a storm. He had an idea that the little spark that he could make was the same thing as the big spark in the cloud.

Thunder and Lightning

BY MARYANNA HEILE

Illustrated by
Seymour Fleishman

In 1752, fifteen years before he went to France to get help for the Colonies, he made a very original and interesting experiment, by which he hoped to find out about lightning.

He knew that if lightning was the same thing as electricity, a key tied to a kite would attract some of it. He was right. The key was struck by a little flash of lightning and the shock traveled down the wet string to his hand.

Since then we have learned much more about lightning.

54

We know that when the moisture in the air condenses on a tiny grain of dust, the little drop in some way becomes charged with electricity. That is, some of the electricity that is always in the air gathers on the little drop of water. Then, when the air gets cold and the little drops flow together to make rain drops, some of the electricity cannot stay on the drops because there isn't room for it and it has to get off. When millions and millions of drops of water are pushing off little bits of electricity, it all goes together and makes up one big flash of lightning. The big flash of lightning is really just millions and millions of tiny little ones.

Flashes of lightning may go from one cloud to another or they may go to the ground. When they go to the ground they sometimes strike trees and split them open. Sometimes they hit a house and set it on fire. They may hit a wire fence and travel along the wire just as electricity travels along a wire to a lamp. If cows or horses are leaning on the wire in a pasture they may all be killed at once.

The lightning may strike a man and kill him. The lightning is very hot, so that if it strikes a house the heat may start a fire there. If it hits a tree the great heat turns the sap into steam so quickly that it must escape and it splits the tree open.

There are a lot of queer old ideas about storms. Open windows do not attract lightning as people used to think. Beds are no safer than chairs. A closet is no safer than anywhere else in the house. Not one person in a million is killed by lightning. Very few houses are ever struck. Therefore, the safest place in a thunderstorm is in the house.

Out of doors the safest place is not under a tree, for trees are often struck. Any tall object may be hit. In open fields and mountains, men have saved themselves by lying flat on the ground.

56

Lightning does not make any sound. It makes the bluish light that everyone sees, like the light of a million lamps all put together. But along with the flash comes a long roll of noise, which people call thunder. It is sometimes so far off that it is just a faint mutter; other times it is so close overhead that it sounds like cannons going off one after the other—so loud and close that it shakes the house.

The noise of the thunder is what frightens people more than the flash of lightning, although the thunder could not possibly do anything any harm.

When the lightning goes through the air it pushes the air away. After it has gone, the air rushes in again to fill up the hole. It is the air rushing in that sets up great waves like sound waves that we hear and call thunder.

The sound of the thunder does not reach us until some time after the lightning flash because, although they occur at the same time, the light waves travel thousands of times faster than the sound waves. We can tell how far the lightning is away by counting the seconds it takes the sound of the thunder to reach us. If it takes the sound five seconds to reach us, the lightning was a mile away. If it takes ten seconds, the flash was two miles away. Before the sound reaches us, the lightning has already struck somewhere.

Sometimes we can see lightning but hear no thunder. The lightning is very far away and the waves of sound have become very weak before they reach the earth and have been caught by the warm air coming up from the ground and carried up again.

Thunderstorms usually come in the afternoon or evening, and sometimes at night. A thundercloud can always be told by its heavy gray and purple look. Just before it starts to rain, a cold wind will come. This is cold air driven in front of the cloud. Thunderclouds are always close to the earth, sometimes not more than a mile up. Airmen can fly over them and see the sun shining on the top. People high up in the mountains can see the storms down along the side of the mountain and hear the thunder and see the lightning while the sun is shining brightly around them.

When thunder rolls in the Catskill Mountains of New York State, the people living around that part of the country tell this story: In 1609 the explorer, Henry Hudson, sailed up the river which now bears his name, looking for a passage to China. Failing to find it, he and his Dutch crew went up into the mountains, where they can be heard to this day, playing the old Dutch game of rolling iron balls at ninepins.

Another story handed down from ancient times to explain thunder is from Norway. The Norwegians thought that one of their gods, Thor, the thunderer, had a great hammer, Miölner, which he hurled through the air against his enemies. It traveled so fast that it made the flash of lightning; and the noise of its striking was the thunder. When thrown, the hammer returned to Thor's hand of its own accord.

Although these tales are fun to read, today we have a great deal of scientific information to explain thunder and lightning; and we find that studying the weather as a science can be even more lively and interesting than the old legends.

58

OBSERVE, report, predict, and warn— these are the things weathermen try to do.

First, let us make a visit to a place where people are observing and measuring the weather.

What do they want to find out? The answer is everything possible, through scientific methods. And everything possible adds up to a good deal. We will list the principal items.

Air pressure	Humidity
Direction of the wind	Amount, kind, and height of clouds
Velocity of the wind	Amount of rain or snow
Temperature of the air	Visibility

All together these elements make up what we call weather. Let us get acquainted with some of the instruments the weathermen use to observe and measure it.

Several of the older instruments catch our eye even before we enter the weather office. They stand outside, high up on top of the building. They are the wind instruments. Nearby we see a rain gauge and a shelter for thermometers.

We will start with the rain gauge, for no doubt it is the oldest weather instrument in the

How We Measure and Observe the Weather

BY IVAN RAY TANNEHILL

Illustrated by Ezra Jack Keats

world. Very early in his career, man the farmer needed to know about rainfall, and he quickly found out how he could measure it. He learned that any open vessel set outdoors would serve as a crude rain gauge. And what he discovered serves us still. Only we have worked out some new ideas.

59

Any straight-sided vessel placed at a distance from trees and other objects that might interfere with the rainfall does pretty well. There is just one trouble. On level ground rain doesn't show much. Even a heavy rain measures only an inch or two. For this reason, a measure even in tenths of an inch is too coarse. We have to be able to measure rain in the hundredths of an inch, for even that small amount of rainfall makes more than a ton of water per acre.

So what do we do?

We catch the rain in a big can, and then empty the water into another can or tube with a bottom one-tenth as big. There is our rain ten times as deep as it was in the big can. Now it is easy to measure the rainfall to the hundredth part of an inch.

Of course, that doesn't tell us *when* the rain fell. A clever device is needed for that, and you may be sure there is one. It is called the tipping bucket. The tipping bucket is a small, flat bucket divided in the middle. It is balanced on a frame and set under a cone-shaped rain spout. When one-hundredth of an inch of rain has come down the spout and run into one side of the bucket, it tips. That much water weighs just enough to tip the bucket and dump the rain into the gauge below. As it tips,

the empty side of the bucket comes under the spout ready to catch the next hundredth of an inch of rain. When the second side of the bucket goes down and dumps, the first side comes under the spout again. The rain itself does all the work.

But this isn't quite all. Electrical wires run from the tipping bucket to a register in the office. Every time the bucket tips, a pen in the office makes a mark on a register sheet. So we know exactly when the bucket tipped each time.

As for snow, we measure it in two ways. One way is to push a stick into the snow on level ground in three places. Then the average of the three is used as the depth of snowfall (un-melted). The other way is to melt the snow collected in the gauge and measure the water. Usually the melting is done by mixing a certain amount of warm water with the snow. Then the melted mixture is measured, and the amount of warm water is subtracted. Ordinarily, when we melt the snow caught in the gauge, the depth of water we get is about one-tenth the depth of the snow.

Now for the wind instruments. One of them is almost as old as the rain gauge and so common that everyone knows it. It is the wind vane. It tells the direction of the wind. Often-times people call it the weather vane because the direction from which the wind blows is a good indication of the coming weather. In former days it was customary to make the wind vane in the shape of a rooster. The modern wind vane gener-ally has an arrow for a head and a wide tail to catch the wind. The arrow points *into* the wind; that is, it points in the same direction the wind is coming from. The weatherman's wind vane is connected by wires into the weather office, where it registers the direction of the wind on a sheet of paper wound around a drum turned by clockwork.

On a short arm just below the wind vane on top of the

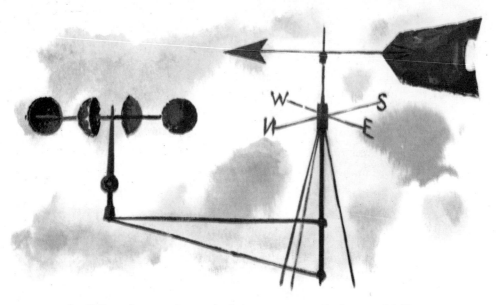

building is another wind instrument. It is a whirling gauge called an *anemometer*. It measures the speed, or velocity, of wind.

The last of the instruments standing outside—but in a special shelter to protect them from sun and rain and snow—are the *thermometers*. A thermometer, as you know, measures heat. A doctor's thermometer measures the heat of the body, but a weatherman's thermometer measures the heat, or the temperature, of the air. In the bulb of the thermometer there is a quantity of mercury. As the bulb is warmed, the mercury in it expands and goes up a narrow bore in the glass. The more the mercury is heated, the higher it rises in the tube.

In the shelter there are quite a few thermometers. One keeps a continuous record of the temperature. It is called a *thermograph* because it makes a graph, or picture, of the temperature changes. This thermometer is quite special. It usually has a curved metal tube instead of glass, and contains alcohol. As the temperature changes, the shape of the tube changes. A recording pen is fastened to one end of the tube.

62

The pen moves as the tube changes shape and makes a mark on a sheet of paper wrapped around a drum. There is clockwork inside it that keeps the paper turning. The sheet of paper is ruled in hours. So the weatherman can tell just what the temperature was at any time during the day or night. Most thermographs will keep a record for a whole week before the sheet has to be changed.

Of course, people always want to know what was the highest temperature in the day and what was the lowest. So in the shelter there are two thermometers that record just that. One thermometer goes up and stays at the highest point reached during the day. It works like a doctor's thermometer. Right above the bulb there is a narrow place in the glass tube. As the temperature of the air rises, the mercury expands and is

forced through the narrow place. When the air gets cooler, the mercury stands still. It can't get down past the narrow place. To get it back into the bulb, the thermometer has to be whirled or shaken.

The other thermometer goes down and stays down at the lowest temperature reached. This thermometer has alcohol in it instead of mercury because alcohol, while it expands and contracts like mercury, freezes at a lower temperature. It can therefore work even when it is very cold. In the glass tube of this alcohol thermometer there is a little piece of glass, called an *index*. The index floats in the alcohol. As the temperature falls, the film at the upper end of the alcohol column draws the index down toward the bulb. When the temperature rises, the alcohol flows up again past the index. But the thermometer is hung on its side, and the index stays down at the low point. Because this thermometer shows the lowest temperature reached, it is called the *minimum thermometer*. The other is called the *maximum thermometer*. In the weather office they are often referred to as *max* and *min*.

In the shelter there is another pair of thermometers. They are wet-and-dry. The dry thermometer gives the temperature of the air. The wet one is so called because around the bulb it has a bit of muslin which the observer wets before he takes a reading. He wets it and sends a stream of air from a fan onto the wet bulb. As the water on the muslin evaporates, it causes the temperature of the wet thermometer to fall. The drier the air the more evaporation and cooling. The observer reads both thermometers and finds the difference between them. From that figure he can get the humidity and the dew point. He doesn't have to work these out. Everything has been figured out for him. All he has to do is refer to a set of tables, and there is his answer.

The pair of wet-and-dry thermometers is also called a *psychrometer*. The psychrometer is very accurate, but it doesn't give a continuous record. So in the weatherman's thermometer shelter there is often another instrument that does that. It is called a *hygrograph*.

A hygrograph works on a very delicate principle. Perhaps you know that a hair grows longer when there is more moisture in the air and shorter when the air is drier. This is the principle on which the hygrograph is made. Strands of human hair are attached to a pen in such a way that as the hair changes length, a mark is traced on a moving piece of paper.

But not all the instruments are out of doors. The pressure of the atmosphere can be measured just as well indoors as outside. The observer can step to the *barometer* in his office and find out what the air pressure is.

The barometer is one of the most important instruments a weatherman has. For changes in air pressure play a very important part in the weather. A drop in the air pressure, for example, may well mean that bad weather is on the way. When the air pressure is rising, you can generally expect fair weather.

The barometer isn't nearly as old as the rain gauge or the wind vane. Still, it is one of the older instruments. It goes back about three hundred years, to the time right after the great astronomer Galileo.

Galileo himself was very much interested in the question of the weight of the atmosphere. He was certain that although invisible, air is a substance and has weight. He made an experiment to prove it. He took a tube of air, plugged it up and weighed it. Then he forced more air into it, plugged it up again, and weighed it once more. The tube weighed a little more. But how much did the atmosphere weigh? Galileo's experiment didn't show that.

It was one of his pupils, Torricelli by name, who thought up a way of showing just how much the atmosphere weighed. He invented the barometer.

Torricelli took a long glass tube closed at one end. He filled it with mercury. Then he put his finger over the open end and turned the tube upside down. He held his finger there to keep the mercury from running out. Then, keeping his finger in place, he set the open end in the bowl containing the mercury. When he took his finger away, a little of the mercury ran out of the tube into the mercury in the bowl, but the column of mercury stayed. The column was nearly 30 inches high. Up at the top was a clear space. It wasn't filled with air because no air could get into the tube. The space was just empty—a vacuum.

Why did the mercury stay up that high in the tube? Because the air outside was pressing on the mercury in the bowl. It was pressing hard enough to push the mercury up nearly 30 inches in the tube. With a shorter tube it would push the mercury right up against the top of the tube. But the air can only push hard enough to hold up 29 or 30 inches of mercury which is very heavy.

Torricelli had discovered how to weigh the atmosphere. But soon afterward another exciting discovery was made. People noticed that the column of mercury in the barometer didn't always stay the same height. Sometimes the mercury was high; sometimes it was low. That must mean the air pressure changed.

Of course, it was easy to understand that if you took the barometer up a mountain, the column of mercury would fall. That was because the air pressure on a mountain was less than at sea level. For there is less air above us the higher up we go. But people noticed that even when the barometer stayed in the same place, the mercury sometimes changed its level in the tube. The air pressure, then, was different at different times. And another thing. The air pressure and the weather seemed to change together. When the mercury was high in the tube, the weather was generally good. When the mercury was low, the weather was bad.

That is how the barometer came into use as an instrument to predict the weather. Barometer makers marked the dial of the barometer to indicate what kind of weather was to be expected. The marks said, "Stormy," "Rain," "Change," "Fair," "Very Dry," and so forth. Such indicators are still used today. They help a little to predict the weather. Modern forecasters, as we shall see, also use other methods. Still, nearly all weather forecasters will tell you the barometer is the most important instrument they have. Whatever else is lacking in a weather forecasting office, you may be sure the barometer is there.

The mercury barometer is the most accurate instrument for measuring air pressure. But it doesn't keep a record. The weatherman needs a record on a sheet of paper so he can see whether the air pressure has been rising or falling and how fast. That's important in forecasting.

For this he uses a *barograph*. It has a metal box with the air taken out, instead of a glass tube with an empty space at the top. The air pushes on the box as it tries to get in. The pressure on the box makes a pen go up or down on a sheet. This works just as well inside the weather office as outside. The air pressure can't be kept out of the office.

It is very handy to have all these dials and registers in the weather office. Then the weatherman doesn't have to run up on the roof every time he gets a phone call asking for the wind direction or velocity, the temperature or the rainfall.

From Season
to Season

The Seasons

BY EDNA L. STERLING

Illustrated by Barbara Tanner

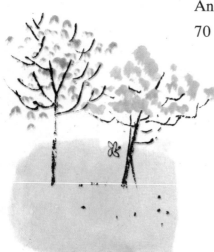

AUTUMN marches across the hill
In russet, red, and gold;
   Winter steals in soft and still
 Crystalline and cold;

   Spring is heard in each bird call
Till everything is green;
   But summer blazes on every wall
And even heat is seen.

70

The Months

BY CHRISTINA ROSSETTI

Illustrated by Barbara Tanner

JANUARY cold desolate;
February dripping wet;
March wind ranges;
April changes;
Birds sing in tune
To flowers of May,
And sunny June
Brings longest day;
In scorched July
The storm-clouds fly,
Lightning-torn;
August bears corn,
September fruit;
In rough October
Earth must disrobe her;
Stars fall and shoot
In keen November;
And night is long
And cold is strong
In bleak December.

71

In Spring

BY MICHAEL LEWIS

Illustrated by Marie Stern

IN Spring the day is early
    And wakes a rosy world,
Where all the twigs are pearly
    And every bud's uncurled.
The birds are up and singing
    Before they can be seen—
And April winds are winging
    Their way to make earth green.

In Spring the sun grows pleasant;
    To prove that he is fond,
He scatters for a present
    Gold coins in every pond.
He sets the bell-flowers ringing
    With perfumed melodies—
And April winds run swinging
    Among the startled trees.

In Spring the night is starry;
    Sleep taps upon the door,
And not a heart is sorry
    Though daylight is no more;
It knows the night is bringing
    Dreams for another day—
And April winds are singing
    The silent hours away.

72

April Is a Dancer

BY SOLVEIG PAULSON RUSSELL

Illustrated by Marie Stern

APRIL comes on tiptoe,
    Tripping through the grass,
Smiling at the little buds
    Who laugh to see her pass.

April comes a-gliding,
    Soft as morning light,
Like a ballerina
    With spangles pure and bright.

April is a dancer;
    Gracefully she twirls,
Spilling warmth and gladness
    From her golden curls.

COLLECTING leaves is a fine hobby. Make prints, press leaves, mount them, and try to find out what trees they come from. There are many books with pictures of leaves which will help you find out the names of the ones you have. One book called *Learn the Trees From Leaf Prints* is easy to use. Turn its pages till you find a leaf exactly like yours. At the end of this book, you will find a list of other books that will be useful.

Twigs or tiny branches in winter give us another clue to a tree's name. Look at tree twigs and you will find that some are hairy, some smooth, some slender and delicate, and others coarse and heavy. The buds on the twigs are different from each other in many ways, too. They may be pointed like the long cigar-shaped buds of the beech. They may be large, oval, brown, and sticky like the horse-chestnut buds. The colors of buds may be yellowish-brown like butternut tree buds, or

How to Know the Trees

BY
MILLICENT E. SELSAM

Illustrated by
D. Alexandroff

red like red maple buds. You cannot learn about twigs and buds all at once. Go at it slowly. Take a few twigs from some trees you know. Mount them on a page of your scrapbook, or on separate hard paper by sewing them on. Look at them closely. Next to each twig write down as much as you can about its buds. The buds may have outer coverings called scales. There may be only a single scale, which is true of the willows, or there may be many scales. Sometimes there are no

74

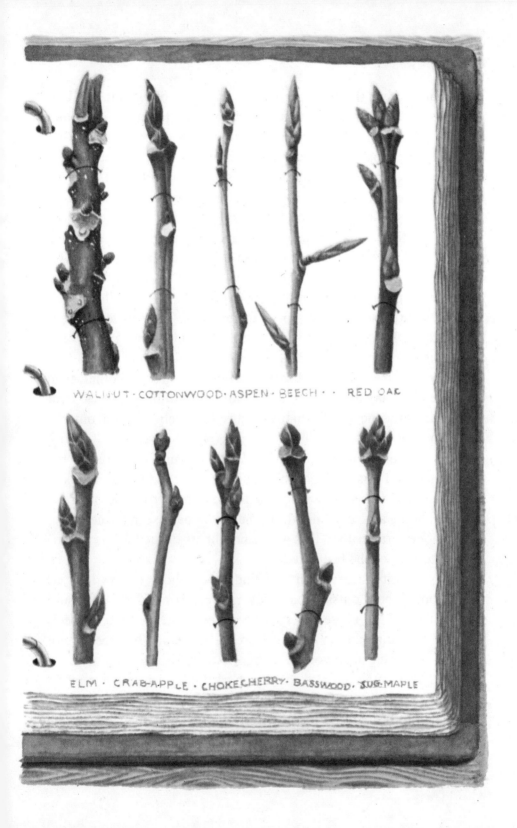

WALNUT · COTTONWOOD · ASPEN · BEECH · · RED OAK

ELM · CRAB-APPLE · CHOKECHERRY · BASSWOOD · SUG·MAPLE

scales at all; the buds are naked like those of walnut and butternut trees. If the buds are hairy or smooth, sticky or round or pointed, write it down. Describe their color, and whether they are clustered or whether each one is alone on the stem.

Next look carefully at the rest of the twig. You have already seen the little circle of scars that mark a year's growth of the twig. Now look for big scars on each side of the stem. Every time a leaf drops off, it leaves this mark or scar, which we call a leaf scar. Now you can become a real detective. Get out your magnifying glass and look at these scars. Compare the scars on the different twigs you have. You will see that these little scars tell a story of their own. They have different shapes. If they are opposite each other on the twig, then that twig came from either a maple, an ash, a dogwood, or a horsechestnut tree. If the leaf scars are not opposite each other, then the twig may have come from a number of different trees. Leaf scars are one of the many things that help us find out the name of a tree.

Some people need only look at the trunk of a tree to tell what kind it is. Look at the trunks of several different kinds of trees and notice how much each one differs from the others.

Some are very smooth. Perhaps you have seen a tree with a smooth gray trunk. This gray smoothness of the bark is a characteristic of the beech tree.

On city streets you will find trees whose trunks look as though their outside bark layers were peeling off like sunburned skin. These are sycamore trees. The outer bark peels off showing patches of white, green, and tan. This tree cannot be mistaken once you have seen its bark.

The outer bark of the shagbark hickory tree peels off in strips. Eucalyptus trees shed their bark in much the same way. The birches can be identified by the color of their bark. The

76

white birch has chalky white bark that peels off sideways around the trunk. Indians once used this bark to make their canoes; but do not strip this bark yourself. Remember that a tree is killed when its bark is removed in a ring around the trunk. The yellow birch has silvery yellow bark that peels off in thin curls. The name of the red birch tree describes its bark color.

Long branching thorns grow out from the trunk and branches of the honey locust tree. Once you know this, you cannot pass one of these trees without recognizing it.

The trees we have mentioned have bark that is easy to recognize. But lots of trees have furrowed bark that looks so much alike it does not help in identifying them until you learn to notice small differences. The names of such trees can be found more easily by following the other clues we have described.

Be sure you cut out and paste and mount as many different drawings and pictures of tree trunks as possible. Work first with the barks that are easy to recognize. Gradually add the harder ones. Slowly but surely you will become one of the people who need only look at the trunk of a tree to tell what kind it is.

WHITE BIRCH · WHITE CEDAR · BEECH · ASPEN ·

The Green Grass
Growing All Around

OLD RHYME   *Illustrated by Marie Stern*

THERE was a tree stood in the ground,
The prettiest tree you ever did see;
The tree in the wood, and the wood in the ground,
And the green grass growing all around.
And the green grass growing all around.

And on this tree there was a limb,
The prettiest limb you ever did see;
The limb on the tree, and the tree in the wood,
The tree in the wood, and the wood in the ground,
And the green grass growing all around.
And the green grass growing all around.

And on this limb there was a bough,
The prettiest bough you ever did see;
The bough on the limb, and the limb on the tree,
The limb on the tree, and the tree in the wood,
The tree in the wood, and the wood in the ground,
And the green grass growing all around.
And the green grass growing all around.

Now on this bough there was a nest,
The prettiest nest you ever did see;
The nest on the bough, and the bough on the limb,
The bough on the limb, and the limb on the tree,
The limb on the tree, and the tree in the wood,
The tree in the wood, and the wood in the ground,
And the green grass growing all around.
And the green grass growing all around.

And in the nest there were some eggs,
The prettiest eggs you ever did see;
Eggs in the nest, and the nest on the bough,
The nest on the bough, and the bough on the limb,
The bough on the limb, and the limb on the tree,
The limb on the tree, and the tree in the wood,
The tree in the wood, and the wood in the ground,
And the green grass growing all around.
And the green grass growing all around.

The Heart of the Tree

BY H. C. BUNNER

Illustrated by Marie Stern

WHAT does he plant who plants a tree?
    He plants the friend of sun and sky;
    He plants the flag of breezes free;
The shaft of beauty, towering high;
He plants a home to heaven a-nigh
    For song and mother-croon of bird
    In hushed and happy twilight heard—
The treble of heaven's harmony—
These things he plants who plants a tree.

June

BY ALICE CROWELL HOFFMAN

Illustrated by Jeanyee Wong

JUNE is drenched with sunshine,
    June is clover sweet,
And June's matchless roses
    Everywhere we meet.

June is all aflutter
    With bejeweled wings.
June is surely made up
    Of life's fairest things.

June is filled with music;
    Songbirds in the trees
Sing their carols gaily
    To the hum of bees.

June is gay with laughter;
    Little folks and tall
Feel the magic gladness
    June spreads over all.

Foolish Flowers

BY RUPERT SARGENT HOLLAND

Illustrated by Mozelle Thompson

WE'VE Foxgloves in our garden;
How careless they must be
To leave their gloves out hanging
Where every one can see!

And Bachelors leave their Buttons
In the same careless way,
If I should do the same with mine,
What would my mother say?
We've lots of Larkspurs in the yard—
Larks only fly and sing—
Birds surely don't need spurs because
They don't ride anything!

And as for Johnny-Jump-Ups—
I saw a hornet light
On one of them the other day,
He didn't jump a mite!

Rain in Summer

BY HENRY WADSWORTH LONGFELLOW

Illustrated by Mozelle Thompson

How beautiful is the rain!
After the dust and heat,
In the broad and fiery street,
In the narrow lane,
How beautiful is the rain!

How it clatters along the roofs,
Like the tramp of hoofs!
How it gushes and struggles out
From the throat of the overflowing spout!

Across the windowpane
It pours and pours;
And swift and wide,
With a muddy tide,
Like a river down the gutter roars
The rain, the welcome rain!

The sick man from his chamber looks
At the twisted brooks;
He can feel the cool
Breath of each little pool;
His fevered brain
Grows calm again,
And he breathes a blessing on the rain.

83

From the neighboring school
Come the boys,
With more than their wonted noise
And commotion;
And down the wet streets
Sail their mimic fleets,
Till the treacherous pool
Ingulfs them in its whirling
And turbulent ocean.

In the country, on every side,
Where far and wide,
Like a leopard's tawny and spotted hide,
Stretches the plain,
To the dry grass and the drier grain
How welcome is the rain!

End of Summer Poem

BY ROWENA BENNETT

THE little songs of summer are all gone today.
The little insect instruments are all packed away:
The bumblebee's snare drum, the grasshopper's guitar,
The katydid's castanets—I wonder where they are.
The bullfrog's banjo, the cricket's violin,
The dragonfly's cello have ceased their merry din.
Oh, where is the orchestra? From harpist down to drummer
They've all disappeared with the passing of the summer.

84

The Mist and All

BY DIXIE WILLSON

Illustrated by
Barbara Tanner

I LIKE the fall,
The mist and all.
I like the night owl's
Lonely call—
And wailing sound
Of wind around.

I like the gray
November day
And bare dead boughs
That coldly sway
Against my pane.
I like the rain.

I like to sit
And laugh at it—
And tend
My cozy fire a bit.
I like the fall—
The mist and all.

Something
Told the Wild Geese

BY RACHEL FIELD

Illustrated by Robert Lawson

SOMETHING told the wild geese
    It was time to go.
Though the fields lay golden
    Something whispered, — "Snow."
Leaves were green and stirring,
    Berries, luster-glossed;
But beneath warm feathers
    Something cautioned, — "Frost."
All the sagging orchards
    Steamed with amber spice,
But each wild breast stiffened
    At remembered ice.
Something told the wild geese
    It was time to fly, —
Summer sun was on their wings,
    Winter in their cry.

Snowflakes

BY HENRY WADSWORTH LONGFELLOW

Illustrated by Robert Lawson

OUT of the bosom of the Air,
  Out of the cloud-folds of her garments shaken,
Over the woodlands brown and bare
  Over the harvest-fields forsaken,
    Silent and soft and slow
    Descends the snow.

87

Frost Work

BY NONA KEEN DUFFY

Illustrated by D. Alexandroff

THERE'S frost work on the window pane
　　And lace work in the trees;
The squirrels in their silver furs
　　Are busier than bees.

Awhile ago the leaves were red
　　As bonfires on a hill,
But now they've turned to chocolate brown
　　And all lie crisp and still.

The puddles where we used to wade
　　Are now all roofed with glass;
The leaves have fallen on our path
　　And crackle as we pass.

The clouds of pearl are far away
　　Against a leaden sky;
The air is light and fresh and sharp,
　　The dome is gray and high.

It was a day, perhaps, like this
　　(Though history doesn't say)
When Pilgrims looked about and planned
　　The first Thanksgiving Day!

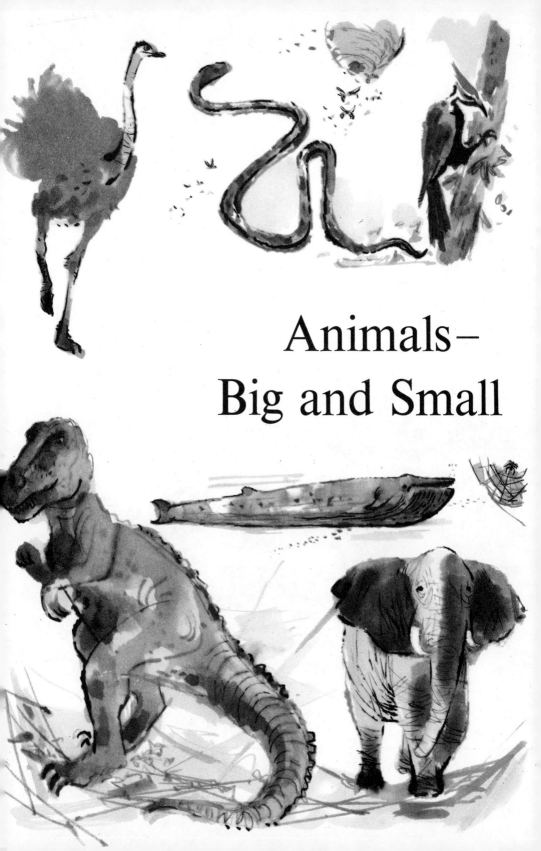

Animals–
Big and Small

Children of the Wind

BY CARL SANDBURG

Illustrated by Ezra Jack Keats

ON the shores of Lake Michigan
high on a wooden pole, in a box,
two purple martins had a home,
and taken away down to Martinique
and let loose, they flew home,
thousands of miles to be home again.

The birds let out began flying
north north-by-west north
till they were back home.
How their instruments told them
of ceiling, temperature, air pressure,
how their control-boards gave them
reports of fuel, ignition, speeds,
is out of the record, out.

Across spaces of sun and cloud,
in rain and fog, through air pockets,
wind with them, wind against them,
stopping for subsistence rations,
whirling in gust and spiral,
these people of the air,
these children of the wind,
had a sense of where to go and how,
how to go north north-by-west north,
till they came to one wooden pole,
till they were home again.

Bird Song

BY LAURA E. RICHARDS

Illustrated by Sabra Mallett Kimball

THE robin sings of willow-buds,
  Of snowflakes on the green;
The bluebird sings of Mayflowers,
  The crackling leaves between;
  The veery has a thousand tales
  To tell to girl and boy;
But the oriole, the oriole,
  Sings, "Joy! joy! joy!"

The pewee calls his little mate,
  Sweet Phoebe, gone astray,
The warbler sings, "What fun, what fun,
  To tilt upon the spray!"
The cuckoo has no song, but clucks,
  Like any wooden toy;
But the oriole, the oriole,
  Sings, "Joy! joy! joy!"

The grosbeak sings the rose's birth,
  And paints her on his breast;
The sparrow sings of speckled eggs,
  Soft brooded in the nest.
The wood thrush sings of peace, "Sweet peace,
  Sweet peace," without alloy;
But the oriole, the oriole,
  Sings, "Joy! joy! joy!"

A Bird

BY EMILY DICKINSON

Illustrated by Sabra Mallett Kimball

A BIRD came down the walk,
He did not know I saw;
He bit an angleworm in halves
And ate the fellow raw.

And then he drank a dew
From a convenient grass,
And then hopped sidewise to the wall
To let a beetle pass.

THERE are many different kinds of pigeons. The dove—the words dove and pigeon were interchangeable in olden days—belongs to one of the smaller species. There is only one family of tame doves—the ring, or collared dove, so-called because of the narrow, dark strip of feathers resembling a collar across the back of his neck. This breed is also called the laughing dove. Instead of the cooing notes of a pigeon, the laughing dove makes sounds similar to soft, chuckling laughter. So contagious is his merriment that it is almost impossible not to laugh with him.

During the courting period he laughs more than ever. His mate joins in, though male pigeons and male doves chatter more than the females. Laughing doves make ideal pets, and are exceptionally pretty and dainty. Some have buff-colored feathers in which delicate shades of lavender are blended, others are gray, while still others are white—and on these the collar mark is a mere shadow.

Couriers of the Sky

BY
MARY GRAHAM
BONNER

Illustrated by D. Alexandrof

The young have all their feathers and are fully grown within three weeks—a week earlier than is customary with pigeons. The doves have as many young and live as long as their pigeon cousins. They require no training, for they are never flown. They have been sheltered for so long that they would be baffled and lost if given their freedom, so they are kept in their pens except when they are taken out for petting. They like to fly to their owner's shoulder, perch on top of his head, and chuckle and laugh over every word he says to them.

There are hundreds of varieties of pigeons. Many of these are featured in pigeon shows. Fantails, dancing and pirouetting with their fan-shaped tails in full display and their chests puffed out, seem to thoroughly enjoy showing off. Every pigeon fancier—no matter what breed he may be exhibiting—will testify to the astonishing manner in which his pets play up to the judges. The more attention the birds receive at home, however, the greater the ease and confidence they show when they are being judged.

The pouter, clown among pigeons, loves to pose. He puffs himself up by breathing air into his crop and frequently topples over when he carries this to excess. As he exhales after one of these performances, he looks as flattened and slim as a deflated balloon. But should he be in a show cage he quickly puffs himself up again. On such occasions he struts more than ever. Although he is called "pouter" he never pouts or sulks, but is a merry bird.

Dragoons, Antwerps, tipplers, and rollers are excellent show birds. They are striking in appearance, and possess strong homing instincts. The roller is a member of the tumbler family, whose amusing antics have long been a source of entertainment, for even the Pharaohs in ancient Egypt had tumblers for pets.

The roller has surpassed the tumbler in his ability to loop, drop, and turn somersaults. He commences turning these in mid-air with such rapidity that it is impossible to count the number of revolutions he makes. At the same time he begins a swift descent toward the earth. With the momentum that he gains it seems certain that he must crash to the ground, but so precise is his timing that in a flash he has stopped turning over,

95

and has straightened his wings to coast with consummate ease to a perfect landing. Students of modern aviation have watched these diverting tricks of the rollers with admiration and envy.

The Jacobins, named centuries ago because their feathered hoods resembled those worn by an order of monks, are the choice of many fanciers. Their ruffs are so elaborate that their faces can hardly be seen.

Each fancier is convinced that his choice is the best. The homer is most widely known and the greatest favorite. The early carrier pigeon, the Antwerp, the dragoon, tippler and those varieties which showed exceptional cleverness, speed and stamina, are his ancestors, and in him are the best traits of each of them. With this background it is not surprising that he is constantly adding new laurels to his fame.

Though all pigeons have the homing instinct, it is more pronounced in the homer and his family than in other breeds. A close relative of the pigeons that are seen in city parks, the

96

homer is more spruce and streamlined in appearance. He is "more on his toes" as the pigeoneers say. His eyes, whether yellow, orange, pearl or ruby red, have a brighter gleam.

Among pigeons, as in families, kinship can often be recognized by a similarity in the color and expression of the eyes. Just as it may be said that a boy has his mother's eyes, so can a pigeon fancier recognize the different families of homing pigeons occupying his loft.

The homer of today used to be known as the carrier pigeon. The carrier pigeon is now bred primarily as a show bird. He is larger than the homer, his neck is longer, and his eyes are encircled by bright red rings. Sometimes the homer is still called a carrier pigeon, but this is incorrect. Pigeon men continually emphasize the fact that the great message bearer of the present is a homer, whose ancestor was the carrier of the past.

A well-known example of the use of one of these carrier pigeons of the past is the dove that was dispatched from the Ark in the time of Noah. When she returned with an olive leaf in her beak Noah knew the waters were receding.

The Arabians give a more detailed account of the flight, for they add that the dove returned with red clay on her feet. This assurance that she had found solid ground made Noah so happy that he prayed that doves would always have red feet to commemorate the end of the flood. Many centuries have passed since the Arabians told of Noah's prayer, but to this day every adult pigeon, no matter what color his feathers may be, has red feet.

It is the homer who competes in long distance flights. He is so intelligent that he knows when he is flying for exercise or when he is racing. In a race he puts all his strength into reaching his loft as swiftly as possible. It is the homer who carries the message back to headquarters when planes are lost in the sea so that the position of the crew may be known. As the men sit, cramped and chilled in their rubber boats or dinghies, they are confident that they will be saved, for the homer is the one link between life and death. Thousands of aviators, whose planes have run out of fuel, or have been shot down by enemy fire, are alive today through the homing faculty and the valor of these birds. Nothing will swerve them from the course which they can follow with such a sure sense of direction. It is little wonder that when the aviator speaks of the homer he always says that the bird has won his wings.

In peacetime homing pigeons show a marked distaste for an East wind, and will wait for a fog to lift if they happen to be out in bad weather. During wartime some extraordinary sense of the imperative nature of their errands makes them fly without faltering through fog, thunder, lightning, dust, bursting shells, or heavy storms. Nor will injury stop them. No homer has ever retreated, so that they have won the lasting respect of all whom they have served.

To a Spider

BY ABIGAIL CRESSON

Illustrated by Joseph Cellini

IF I were you
    I'd never stay
In such a corner
    Every day.
In dust and dark—
    Not I! I'd spin
A web all silver
    Fine and thin.

I'd film it
    On a daisy's face
Or spread it
    On the grass like lace.
But, oh, I'd have it
    In the air
With sunshine,
    Sunshine everywhere.

The wind might
    Tear it, yes—but then
I'd get to work
    And spin again.
This much I know,
    I'd never stay
Inside four walls
    On such a day.

99

The Butterfly and the Caterpillar

*A Fable Old
Is Here Retold*

BY JOSEPH LAUREN

Illustrated by Barbara Tanner

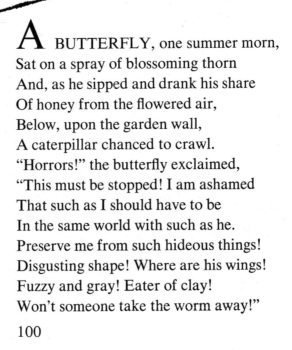

A BUTTERFLY, one summer morn,
Sat on a spray of blossoming thorn
And, as he sipped and drank his share
Of honey from the flowered air,
Below, upon the garden wall,
A caterpillar chanced to crawl.
"Horrors!" the butterfly exclaimed,
"This must be stopped! I am ashamed
That such as I should have to be
In the same world with such as he.
Preserve me from such hideous things!
Disgusting shape! Where are his wings!
Fuzzy and gray! Eater of clay!
Won't someone take the worm away!"

The caterpillar crawled ahead,
But, as he munched a leaf, he said,
"Eight days ago, young butterfly,
You wormed about, the same as I;
Within a fortnight from today
Two wings will bear me far away,
To brighter blooms and lovelier lures,
With colors that outrival yours.
So, flutter-flit, be not so proud;
Each caterpillar is endowed
With power to make him by and by,
A blithe and brilliant butterfly.
While you, who scorn the common clay,
You, in your livery so gay,
And all the gaudy moths and millers,
Are only dressed-up caterpillars."

IT is the katydid and cricket that really do the finest fiddling, though perhaps old Aesop's fable has made the grasshopper more famous for it. Most of the insect music that we hear in summertime is made by these two more talented relations.

Now the names of grasshoppers and katydids and crickets are confused and most misleading. Names given them by ordinary mortals like you and me are all mixed up with the names applied by scientists. And the scientific names seem badly muddled up amongst themselves. We are told that the insects we call grasshoppers are more truly locusts. True grasshoppers, the scientists assert, are katydids; and cave-crickets are really katydids which live in caves. Yet katydids, which are not locusts, have the scientific name *Locustidae,* meaning "of the locust family." Incidentally the so-called seventeen-year locusts aren't locusts but cicadas, sap-sucking bugs.

Insect Music

BY WILFRID S. BRONSON

Illustrated by
Wilfrid S. Bronson

All this is much too complicated, except perhaps for scientists. And so I'm going to risk making confusion worse confounded by trying now to simplify it all, that is, for the convenience of our simpler-minded selves. The insects most of us call grasshoppers have, among other features, much shorter feelers than insects almost anyone would label katydids. Some of the latter are known as meadow grasshoppers, but to anyone who has ever seen a tree-katydid or a bush-katydid, these slender-legged, long-feelered insects from the fields are meadow-katydids. And the so-called cave-crickets are wingless katy-

102

dids which live in caves. So cave-katydids let us call them, reserving the name of cricket for insects that really are crickets.

After the spring peepers and trilling toads have ended their great choruses, and after the birds have been singing for some time, more and more the insect instrumentalists take up the tune. By mid-summer, when many birds have ceased their singing, the grasshoppers and katydids and crickets are in a great crescendo that goes on day and night with never an interruption. Theirs is the greatest orchestra on earth. It's stupendous, it's colossal! It reaches from the tropics to the Arctic and from sea to sea. It plays from dawn to dark to dawn, and on and on. A few dozen players may stop fiddling as you pass along, but billions more continue undisturbed. As some take time out for their meals and rest, others fall to work with renewed energy. There are no union hours and no dues. All insects which have instruments may play as much or little as they please, however good or bad musicians they may be.

Actually, of course, the insects are not interested in orchestra playing, each one only intent on making itself heard. Nevertheless, insect music is like that of a mighty orchestra in that it

is produced with instruments by many players, all following a great conductor. This conductor is a temperamental fellow, familiar to us all. His name is Old Man Weather. With many variations on the theme he may call for pianissimo with a sudden chill in one section, while working up fortissimo with furious heat in another. At the end of the piece he compels diminuendo and finally silence, with a wave of his frosty fingers in the fall.

Clearly and often loudly though the insects play, people who live in the country are apt not to hear them even after dark, when daytime noises have quieted down, unless they listen purposely. For, like dinner music which sets everybody talking, this insect playing rarely interrupts our rural thoughts while possibly it stimulates them. The "chirping of the bugs" is so over-stimulating to some city people, who never before have heard these noisy relatives of the silent cockroach, that they have to go back to the clamor they are used to for a good night's sleep.

As with grasshoppers, it is only male katydids and crickets that play, and, by his fiddling, each expresses his emotions, whatever they may be. Sometimes, as when a human being whistles, it is perhaps just happiness and his own good health. Sometimes he may be trying to enchant a female; but if he responds to the playing of another male, it is only to outdo him if he can, and probably never to join in a duet.

But louder than all others in the nighttime playing is the broad-winged or leaf-winged katydid. All the rest play but a poor second fiddle to this one, which carries on the whole night long with the noise that sounds like "Katy did!" and "Katy did! She did!"

Now Katy's deed undoubtedly was done a very long time ago, for these insects have been telling about it for as long as

104

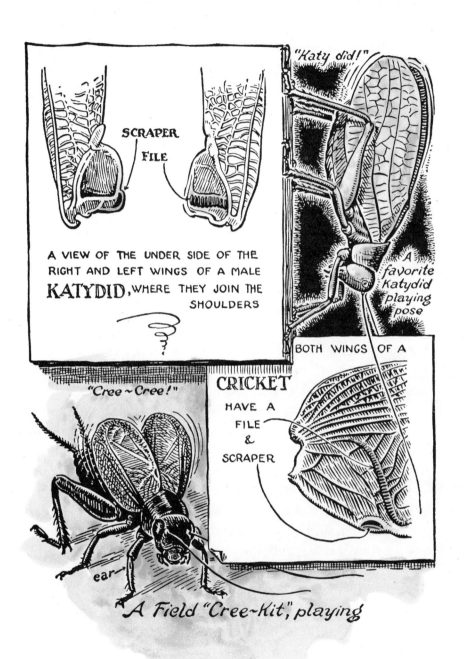

"Katy did!"

SCRAPER

FILE

A VIEW OF THE UNDER SIDE OF THE RIGHT AND LEFT WINGS OF A MALE KATYDID, WHERE THEY JOIN THE SHOULDERS

A favorite Katydid playing pose

BOTH WINGS OF A

CRICKET

HAVE A FILE & SCRAPER

"Cree~Cree!"

ear

A Field "Cree-Kit," playing

English-speaking people can remember, in fact much longer. They were saying "Katy did" before either of these two words belonged to human language.

Whatever it was that the unidentified but over-active Katy so definitely did do, we are never told. Of course, it may have been something too terrible to mention.

There are people who claim that some of the insects say "Katy didn't, she didn't, didn't!" But it's not worth arguing about as long as no one knows what she is supposed to have or not to have done. Listen to their racket in the trees on late summer evenings and decide for yourself who says what and who is ahead and, if possible, who is right. Probably both sides are, the didders and the didn'ters. Katy doubtless did a lot of things, and there were things she didn't do.

In New England many people say that Katy isn't even mentioned, that the katydids simply squawk three times, and let it go at that. And in the South the calls of katydids are not considered English either. Their name down there is Cackle-Jack.

As far as I am concerned, their rasping sounds are like the creaking of old-fashioned buggy springs, or even like some of the body squeaks in modern cars. Perhaps this is only natural since all these sounds are produced by one unlubricated surface rubbing on another. Unlike grasshoppers, katydids and crickets do not use their legs in fiddling, but play on one wing with the other. In the katydid's case it's the left wing with its file-like row of ridges rubbing over the right wing with its hard little scraper just behind the shoulders, where the wings overlap. From there the wings bulge backward on either side and act as amplifiers. Usually the tattle-tale music is made with the performer facing head down along a leaf or twig, the wings slightly ajar, just free of the body.

The cricket plays in almost any position but with its right

106

wing over its left, though there appears to be an equally good file and scraper on either wing. Maybe it can reverse and play like a katydid when its wings grow weary in the customary cricket posture. Maybe there is about the same proportion of "left-handed" crickets as left-handed people.

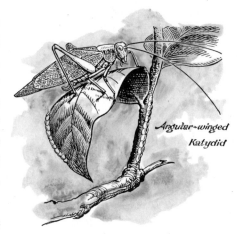

Angular-winged
Katydid

Katydids and crickets have a slit in each front shin. Inside are air spaces and eardrums, and these are the hearing apparatus with which one katydid or cricket listens to another. Some female insects seem to have ears only for the "voice" of the male. But katydids must have their receiving sets tuned to other things as well, for they stop their own noise at the sound of your voice or even your footfall underneath their tree.

Though cautious in this way, katydids are calmer and not as jumpy as grasshoppers. We seldom disturb or even see the broad-winged katydids, because of their preference for the tops of trees. It seems to be their attitude that katydids should not be seen, but heard. Many are not even seen by the ever-hungry, sharp-eyed birds, because they are so leaf-like both in shape and color. Often all they have to do to escape detection is sit still.

If a bird does see a katydid and makes ready for a meal, the big green insect suddenly swells and rasps right in its enemy's face. This may be enough to scare away the smaller birds. And if, on a rare occasion, you may meet this high-tree katydid close at hand and pick it up, it will surely try to bite you.

107

WHAT does "wax" make you think of? Candles? Polishing floors? There's wax in your mother's lipstick and in the cold cream that you rub into your chapped hands and face. This wax is beeswax. The bees make it and build their homes with it.

If we wanted to be technical, we might almost say, "In the United States, only the bumblebees are wax makers" because the honeybees are not native American insects. Their original home was Europe. They came to this country on sailing ships, accompanying the first settlers in Massachusetts and Virginia. They supplied the colonists with sugar for their tea and wax for their candles. Indians, who made sugar from the sap of maple trees, called the honeybee "the white man's fly."

No honeybee ever builds or lives alone. Its whole existence is a cooperative one. Most of the citizens of the hive are workers, half an inch long, with heart-shaped heads and hairy, winged bodies. Each has a long, curving tongue

They Build with Wax

BY
DOROTHY STERLING

Illustrated by
D. Alexandroff

that can reach deep into a flower to suck its nectar. Each has a honey stomach to carry the sweet stuff home. When pollen from the blossoms collects on a worker's fine hairs, she combs her fur with her spiny legs and packs the yellow powder into pockets in her hind pair of legs. These are her pollen baskets. From the antennae on her head, with which she smells, to the sting which protrudes from her abdomen, the worker's body is equipped with the tools and chemicals needed to carry on the work of the hive.

108

Any sunny day when there are flowers in bloom you can watch a worker collecting nectar and stuffing her baskets with bright yellow pollen. If you want to meet the rest of the family, you must visit them at home. The male bee, called a *drone,* is longer and broader than his sister, but he has neither sting, pollen basket, nor a tongue for sucking nectar. In a field of clover, he would starve to death. He lives only to fertilize the eggs of the queen. All summer long his sisters feed him honey. In the fall, when the last flowers are fading and the family food supply must be saved for the cold months ahead, the workers push the drones out of the hive, leaving them to die.

The most important citizen in the bee home is the queen. Without her there would be no family. Almost twice as long as the worker, slenderer than the burly drone, she is an egg-laying machine. She can lay her own weight in eggs in a single day. Although she lives for three or four years—producing more than a million offspring—she never builds or gathers food. A circle of workers surrounds her at all times, feeding her from their own mouths when she is hungry, cleaning her, and keeping her warm.

In January or February, even in the North, the queen starts laying eggs again. When the first pussy willows are in bloom, the workers fly from the hive. Their job now is to collect pollen, the breakfast food on which their baby sisters and brothers thrive. The grown-ups' honey and the babies' pollen are both gathered from flowers.

The rows of nursery rooms are soon filled with comma-shaped gray eggs. Even before the eggs hatch, worker nurses put food in these rooms. The first meals for all bee babies consist of a white cream known as *royal jelly*. Royal jelly is neither honey nor pollen, but a concentrated food made inside the worker bees. Remember the cod-liver oil or viosterol which you had to take as a baby? Royal jelly is something like this. Perhaps if your vitamin oil had had such a fancy name, you would have liked it better.

Worker and drone babies receive royal jelly for only two or three days. Then they are put on a diet of pollen and honey. The hatched larvae look much like the wasp grubs, pale, wingless, and legless. At first they lie curled up, head to tail, but as they grow they straighten out until their heads fill the entrance of their rooms. Nurse bees feed them tirelessly, bringing them 1,300 meals a day!

Five or six days after the baby has hatched, its grown-up

110

sisters cover the cradle with a door of wax. Inside, the larva spins a silk blanket around itself. For twelve days it rests and changes in its cocoon until it is an adult worker bee.

Outdoors, the honey flow is on in fields and gardens. Inside, the hive is crowded with brood (the eggs and larvae of the bees are called *brood*), and every day is a birthday for a thousand more eager workers. It's time to think about dividing up the family and starting a new home. But before the move can be made, there's work to be done.

The cradle cells of the worker bees are small. They average five to an inch, and the caps which cover them are almost flat. Now, larger cells are built, only four of them fitting into an inch of space. In these the queen lays unfertilized eggs. When these babies hatch, they are even hungrier than the worker babies and must be fed three days longer. When they spin cocoons, their nurses build dome-shaped caps on their rooms. They will soon be drones.

In another part of the hive, an entirely new kind of room is being built. An ordinary egg has been laid in an ordinary cell along the edge of the comb. A crew of workers add bits of wax to its side walls, changing the six-sided cell into a rounded cup. Often there are three or four of these cups in a row, looking like little upside-down volcanoes. These are the cradles for new queens.

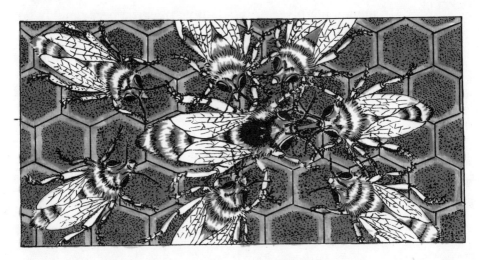

Nothing is too good for royalty in the bee world. Instead of switching the three-day-baby from royal jelly to the worker diet of pollen, her majesty's nurses continue to feed her great quantities of white cream. It is this rich diet, her only baby food, which transforms the grub into a royal mother.

As she grows, the builders plaster more and more wax around her. The finished job is an inch and a half long and corrugated like the sides of a thimble.

When these peanut-shaped cells are completed it's time for moving day. The new queen will stay at home while the old queen leaves. Thousands of worker bees stuff themselves with stored honey. They eat until they can eat no more—like Thanksgiving dinner. Then they fly from the hive.

There is a buzzing of wings as the crowd streams upward into the sunlight. The noisy cloud of bees soon settles on a convenient branch to wait until they have located a good spot in which to build. Sometimes the swarm lands on a rooftop or even on the engine of a moving train. Filled with honey and the excitement of moving, the bee cluster is in a friendly mood and can usually be handled without fear of stings.

Scout bees fly ahead of the group, sometimes even days before the swarming. As soon as they signal that they've found a new home site, the others follow. The family flies together over trees and housetops, like an enormous dark ball.

In man-made hives or in a hollow tree, the bees quickly go to work. Their short holiday is over and their dark new home must be furnished. Wax is the first requirement and it is manufactured in a curious way.

A worker clings to the side walls or roof of the hive. A second grasps her hind legs. A third and a fourth bee hitch on to the chain until a bridge of bees stretches from wall to wall. Each bee holds on with her front feet to the hind feet of the

112

bee nearest her. More and more chains are started until there is a hanging curtain of bees.

The workers hang for as long as twenty-four hours, until the chemical factories in their bodies have produced wax. No one knows exactly how this is done, but the honey they have eaten and the heat produced by their closely packed bodies are necessary in the manufacturing process. The wax oozes out of eight tiny pockets on the underside of each bee in the chain. It is a liquid which quickly hardens into pearly, pear-shaped flakes.

The scales of wax are brittle and almost as clear as glass. With her spiny legs, she pokes them out of her pockets and passes them forward to her mouth. Mixing them with saliva, she chews them until they are soft. Then, with the wax in her mouth, she flies to the roof of the hive and plasters it there. Bee after bee adds a bit of wax. Other workers who have not been part of the chain pinch the material with their jaws and pat it out until floor and walls take shape and the first six-sided cell is complete.

Another cell is built, and another, each one a matching marvel of insect engineering. The comb hangs from the roof like a picture on a wall. Back to back to the first one, a second comb is added so that a single layer of wax forms the bottom of two rows of cells. The structure is incredibly light and incredibly strong. The walls are so thin that it takes three thousand of them, laid on top of each other, to form an inch in thickness. Yet one pound of wax comb will hold more than twenty-five pounds of honey.

To test the skill of the bee builders, try an experiment with the dripping from a candle. You need not chew it if you don't want to. You can warm it between your fingers until the lump is soft enough to mold. Now flatten it out and shape it. Even with tweezers or a pointed pencil the best you can produce is a thick, awkward cup. Compare this with the delicate, regular pattern of the rooms in the comb. Bee cells are constructed with such unfailing accuracy that a scientist once suggested that they be used as a unit of measure, instead of an inch or centimeter.

Even before the cells are completed the queen starts laying eggs. Soon there are young workers in the new home. As their faces poke through the thin doors of their rooms, they make you think of the trained dogs in the circus who jump through paper-covered hoops.

For two or three weeks, these downy creatures stay indoors, working at first as nurses and cell cleaners, later as wax makers and builders. They share the housework long before they try out their gauzy wings. The rest of their short lives—only six weeks in the busy midsummer months—will be spent in the fields, collecting pollen and nectar.

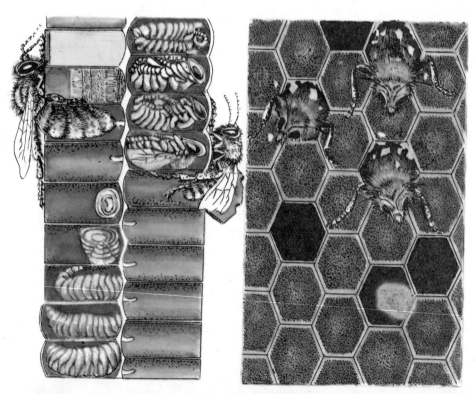

AN ant is like us because it is alive. It can run and see and feel. It breathes, gets hungry, builds a home and brings up children. But an ant is an insect. Its body is made in sections. The parts of its body are separated by such a thin neck and waist that it looks as though it were almost cut in three. The first section is the head, the second is the chest (called *thorax*), and the third is the abdomen.

In the head, as in our own, are the ant's brains, its mouth and eyes. In its mouth are tongue and jaws. But instead of working up and down as ours do, the ant's jaws move from each side to the middle. The eyes are rather different from our own. They are made up of many smaller eyes and cannot be rolled about as ours can. We view a horse standing still just as readily as a horse galloping. If the horse is still, our eyes move very quickly all over him. We get a good idea

What Is an Ant?

BY WILFRID S. BRONSON

Illustrated by Wilfrid S. Bronson

of his shape. But when an ant looks at a resting grasshopper its eyes cannot move to view it thoroughly. The ant's idea of what the hopper looks like is much more clear when the hopper moves a little.

On the head also are the ant's two noses, the feelers used for smelling. They also serve as fingers, the ant touching whatever interests it to learn its nature through the feel. But these are not its only fingers. Growing out of its chest section, the ant has (instead of two arms) six legs. Often it uses its front feet as we do our hands, to touch things, to grasp them, to lift, to push and pull. And its jaws are also used for grasping, lifting, pushing and pulling. So we might say the ant has fingers all over its face and chest.

On the back of their chest section some ants have wings. These are the royalty, the young princes and princesses at the beginning of their lives as grown-ups. The long lacy wings of a princess ant are like the filmy veil a bride wears to her wedding and removes forever once she is married and queen of her own new home. The princess ant flies to her wedding and takes off her wings when she is ready to start a home and family of her own.

In the third section, the abdomen, are an ant's two stomachs, one much larger than the other. The small one is for its own use. The large one is a shopping bag in which it brings home food for other ants. There is quite a difference in the size of these two stomachs—one private, the other public.

An ant has jointed legs and so do we. But the ant's joints are on the outside while ours are inside. The hard armor worn by the ant is its only skeleton; it has no bones. "In days of old when knights were bold" they imitated insects with the metal armor which they wore. A knight oiled his armor to keep it from rusting and squeaking. The tidy ant shines its armor often with its oily saliva. For that matter, many people use olive oil to clean their skins. Many use oily cold creams, and in Africa a woman will put rancid butter on her head, letting it melt down over her body. The knight breathed through his helmet, but the ant breathes through two rows of holes in the sides of its armor. Tubes carry the air from these holes into all parts of its body, for it has no lungs. When we breathe in, our lungs swell like toy balloons, and shrink as the air goes out again. Ants breathe by moving their abdomens like accordions. You can notice this more easily by watching the ant's bigger relative, the wasp.

116

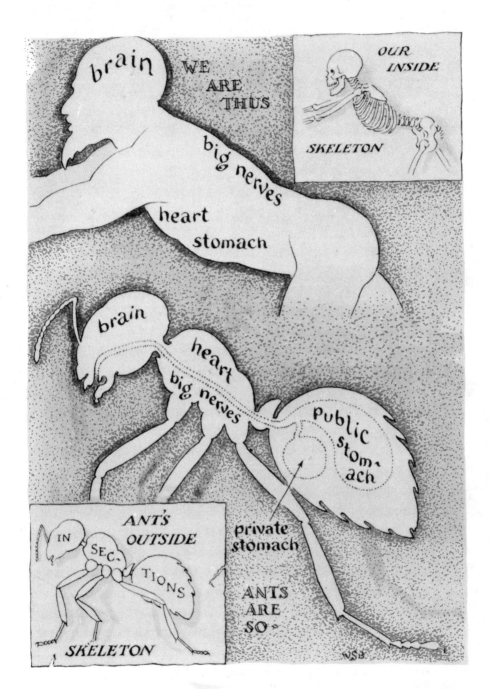

117

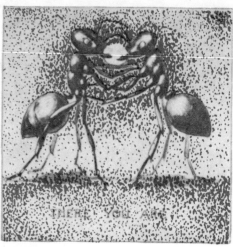

Before oiling itself an ant removes dust from its head and feelers. For this it has a fine pair of combs on each foreleg. The teeth of the combs meet and the feeler is pulled between them. But whereas we may remove a stray hair from a comb with our fingers, the ant must clean its combs in its jaws.

All through our bodies we have nerves, but the biggest ones are in our backs. The ant's big nerves run down its underside. The heart of an ant, instead of being in its chest, is in the middle of its back.

Though ants work very hard they take time to play sometimes. They wrestle with each other and may roll a grain of wheat around for the same fun we take in playing ball. There are ants which stop their work to gather as at a great convention. They all sit gently waving their feelers, which may be the way they listen at a meeting. No one knows how ants hear. Their "ears" have never been found. Perhaps the feelers are not only noses and fingers, but ears as well. Maybe they are

118

like portable radio receiving sets. At least we know the ants do hear, but what the meetings are about is still a mystery.

The meetings may have something to do with the government of their ant country to which all are very loyal. Just as the ant's public stomach is much larger than its own, so it cares more for the good of its country than for its own good. Each ant, though fond of sweet food, gathers most of it for the use of other citizens. And though it wishes to go on living, yet it will fight and even die to save the lives of its people.

In any field there may be several different ant nations. A number of cities may belong to one nation if their Queens are sisters. One ant can tell another's nationality by its smell. All ants of one nation smell the same. Ants which do not smell alike are foreigners to each other, and may be enemies. Each nation claims a certain region as its land and no other kind of ant is supposed to trespass there. They do not put up "No trespassing, no hunting" signs, but they have scouts who patrol the border. These use a trespasser very badly. Or should a whole nation of enemy ants be about to trespass to attack the scouts' own cities, they rush home to give the alarm. There is no time to tell each citizen by feeler tap-talking. They bang their heads against the walls of their tunnels as we might strike a fire-bell. It is just as though they shouted, "Call out the guard!" Everybody knows at once what is wrong and they get ready to fight off the attack.

Of all insects, ants are no doubt the smartest. Thousands of them, united, form great nations, with a very useful language, and a government, vast numbers of hard-working people and their own armies of soldiers. The smartest animals which have backbones and inside skeletons are men. Men have nations, language, government, vast numbers of working people and armies. This is true only of ants and men.

SOME people keep snakes as pets even though they are not very intelligent or active.

If you want to have a snake for a pet, find out first whether any poisonous kinds may be found in the vicinity. Then make sure you can identify a poisonous one. If you are in doubt, leave them alone. Look for snakes in fields, open woods, and along streams. Turn over rocks and old logs. Move quietly because snakes can feel the vibrations as you walk. If you do find a snake and are sure it is not poisonous, grab it right back of the head, since that will keep it from biting.

Snakes

BY HERBERT S. ZIM

Illustrated by Elaine Sand

Some snakes are tame enough to pick up and handle immediately. Others tame down after they have been handled a while. When you hold a snake, support its body by letting it lie partly on your hands or arm. Some snakes are unhappy in captivity. If they do not tame easily, it is best to let them go.

Any simple wooden box will do to house a pet snake. Equip the box with a sliding glass front and a dozen small ventilation holes around the sides and you have a fine cage. Snakes do not need much room. A cage about ten inches wide, twenty-four inches long, and ten inches high is fine for most medium-sized snakes. A heavy glass dish two or three inches deep, half filled with water, does for drinking and bathing. A rock or branch to crawl over and a sprinkling of sand on the floor are all the furnishings you need.

Feeding a pet snake is a problem, for snakes eat live food and some will not eat in captivity. Earthworms are good food

for some small snakes, frogs for some medium-sized kinds. Racers, milk, bull rat, and king snakes often eat mice. A snake that eats well during the warm months may go through the winter without food, even though it does not hibernate. Sometimes a snake can be trained to eat small pieces of meat or fish if they are wiggled in front of its nose or pushed into its mouth.

Well-fed snakes in dry cages are likely to stay healthy. Some may develop skin infections if the floor of the cage is wet. Wash any sore spots in a mild germ-killing solution. When a snake gets ill, it's usually best to turn it loose.

Four Little Foxes

BY LEW SARETT

Illustrated by Robert Frankenberg

SPEAK gently, Spring, and make no sudden sound;
For in my windy valley, yesterday I found
New-born foxes squirming on the ground—
      Speak gently.

Walk softly, March, forbear the bitter blow;
Her feet within a trap, her blood upon the snow,
The four little foxes saw their mother go—
      Walk softly.

Go lightly, Spring, oh, give them no alarm;
When I covered them with boughs to shelter them from harm,
The thin blue foxes suckled at my arm—
      Go lightly.

Step softly, March, with your rampant hurricane;
Nuzzling one another, and whimpering with pain,
The new little foxes are shivering in the rain—
      Step softly.

122

DINOSAURS were the strangest animals that ever existed on this earth. They were the sort of creatures you might think of as inhabiting another planet or the kind you dream of in a bad nightmare. The word dinosaur means "terrible lizard." It is a good description. Dinosaurs were reptiles, cold-blooded animals related to crocodiles, snakes and lizards. At one time they ruled the entire world.

Some were of gigantic size, heavier than a dozen elephants. Those had long snake-like necks, small heads, and twenty-foot tails. They waded along the margins of lakes and rivers, half sunk in mud and water, feeding on soft plants.

Introducing Dinosaurs

BY
ROY CHAPMAN ANDREWS

Illustrated by Thomas W. Voter

Others walked on powerful hind legs, and stood as tall as a palm tree. Their small arms ended in clutching hands and curved claws longer than those of the biggest bear. Their mouths were more than a yard deep, bristling with great dagger-like teeth. They killed other dinosaurs and tore the flesh off their bodies, gulping it in hundred-pound chunks.

Some were huge, pot-bellied reptiles thirty feet long. They walked erect, balanced by heavy tails. Their faces were drawn out and flattened into wide, horny beaks like a duck's bill. Two thousand small teeth filled their mouths. They loved to wallow in lakeshore mud, chewing plants and herbs. But they were good swimmers, too. When a hungry flesh-eater leaped out of the forest, they dashed for the deepest water where he couldn't follow.

Other dinosaurs were short-legged and square-bodied, as big as an army tank. Long horns projected forward like two machine guns from a bony shield over an ugly hooked beak. They lumbered through the jungle, and all other animals fled in terror.

Another fantastic reptile carried a line of triangular plates down the middle of its back. On the tip of the ten-foot tail were four huge spikes, three feet long. At the same time there lived a dinosaur completely armored by a heavy shell. Its thick tail ended in a huge mass of bone. He could swing it like a war club and give a crushing blow.

Some dinosaurs were slender and swift, skipping over the plains faster than a race horse. And some were very small, no larger than rabbits. They hid among the rocks or in the thickest forest for protection.

What I tell you about these unbelievable creatures is true. They really did live. We know they did because we find their bones buried in the earth. These bones have been fossilized or turned to stone.

Also we find their footprints in stone. It is just as if you had stepped in soft mud, and the tracks your feet made had become solid rock. In the same way the impressions of plants and trees and insects have been preserved in stone. So we know what the country was like when the dinosaurs lived.

The time was the Age of Reptiles. That was a period in the earth's history which began 200 million years in the past and ended 60 million years ago. When we talk about millions of years, it is difficult to get a real mind-picture of that vast length of time. Ape-like human beings did not exist until one million years ago. Our recorded history is hardly 7,000 years old. The time back to the Age of Reptiles is like the distance in miles separating us from the moon.

People often ask if there are any dinosaurs living today. The answer is, no. They all died out at the end of the Age of Reptiles. Why they disappeared we don't know. We only know they did. When you see pictures in the "funnies" of dinosaurs with men, that is all imagination. No human being ever saw a dinosaur alive. They had become extinct 60 million years before man came upon the earth.

The Age of Reptiles lasted 140 million years. During that great length of time dinosaurs

125

ruled the land. In the air weird goblin-like reptiles sailed through the gloomy skies. Some of them had long faces, peaked heads and twenty-foot wings. They make one think of fairy-tale witches flying on broom-sticks.

The oceans swarmed with other reptiles. There were great sea serpents with wide flat bodies, long slender necks, and small heads filled with sharp teeth. There were also giant lizards, forty feet long, and others that looked like fish. Truly the land, the sea and the air were frightening in the Age of Reptiles.

But the earth back in that far dim past was not as it is to-day. The climate was different. In most places it was tropical or sub-tropical like southern California or southern Florida. The climate was the same al-most everywhere. There were no cold winters. If there had been, the reptiles could not have flourished the way they did. They didn't like cold weather. In those days the weather was warm and humid the year round. Thick jungles, low lands and swamps stretched across most of the world.

In the Age of Reptiles the great mountain systems had not yet been born. The Himalayas, now the highest mountain range in the world, did not exist. There were no Rocky Mountains. Instead the low lying country of western America and of central Europe held great inland seas. What is now the state of Kansas was covered with water. Also Wyoming and Montana. The land lifted at times and sank and rose again. One hundred and forty million years is a long time, and many changes took place.

Our geography books would not have been of much use then. The continents then were not as they are today. There were land connections which do not exist at the present time. North America and Asia doubtless had a wide land bridge across the Bering Straits. North and South America were more broadly united than today. Possibly North America and Europe were joined across Greenland and Iceland. Europe and Africa were connected where the Mediterranean Sea now separates them. Asia and Australia were joined by land in what is now the East Indies.

This is the way we think 'the world geography looked during much of the Age of Reptiles. You can see, therefore, that animals could have traveled from one continent to another. They were not cut off by the climate, mountains and oceans that exist today.

That is the reason why dinosaur bones are found over much of the world. They have been discovered in North and South America from Canada to Patagonia, in various parts of Europe, in Africa and Asia, and even in Australia.

MY first introduction to the King of Beasts came as a great surprise and, strangely enough, after I had been looking for him for five long months. During this time we had traveled far and wide over the great Central African Plateau which for centuries has been the lion's ancestral domain, yet not a glimpse had we had of this royal beast. I had begun to think that there were no lions left in Africa, when a journey into Western Tanganyika, their last stronghold, crowded five weeks of my life brimful of lion adventure.

I was driving our little camera car through a vast meadow of yellow grass. It was radiator-high and gleamed like fields of ripening wheat. On one trampled patch a score of vultures fought and wrangled over a little pile of clean white bones. The sun was just touching the meridian. Waves of heat, undulating and golden as the shimmering grass, rolled over all the landscape. My dazzled eyes sought relief in watching

Lion

Adventures

BY CARL AND MARY
L. J. AKELEY

Illustrated by
Joseph Cellini

the dark contrasting shadows lying dense beneath the few and isolated trees that here and there relieve the monotony of the rolling veldt. Suddenly in the deep gray shade cast by a rankly growing table-top acacia standing high on an abrupt rise of ground, three darker shadows seemed to move. It might easily be only the heat waves, I thought, blurring my eyes and distorting even familiar objects—hummocks, stones and ant hills. But plainly, three objects again lifted themselves as I steered

128

in their direction and then slowly sank back into the protecting grass. I drove on. When but fifty yards away, the three shadows resolved themselves into three glorious living creatures. Three massive, tawny heads turned inquiringly in our direction. Three powerful, sinewy bodies shifted but slightly at our approach. The lion, well up on a vantage point, and wearing a splendid copper-colored mane, now lifted his head a little higher. His companions, two glossy lionesses of paler hue, rested motionless by his side. For several minutes we strained our eyes at them very cautiously, our guns in hand. Then as they gave no sign of nervousness or fear nor any show of hostility or of giving ground, we studied them through our glasses while they, still in repose, were equally intent on watching us. We could plainly see their whiskers, their large and yellow eyes, and could observe their even breathing as they, replete with the night's feast, waited patiently for us to

travel on. After staying near them until our discretion urged us to move along, I started the noisy motor of our car. As we slowly drove away the big lion stood up to watch us out of sight. And while the veldt widened between us and them we turned and saw the great beast still standing on the hillock looking the country over. Doubtless in a moment he would rejoin his mates and they would quickly settle down, grateful for the opportunity to continue their morning's interrupted sleep. After many weeks of safari I had at last seen my first lion. Never before had I been so thrilled as by the simple, yet exalted, dignity of this monarch of the wilds.

One day, three weeks later, in this same Tanganyika wilderness, my husband and I started off for a holiday. We had collected several groups for the American Museum of Natural History and had photographed a native lion-spearing show—the most stirring primitive drama of all Africa. We had seen many lions at close range and had had experiences few have ever had before. To hope for more would indeed be asking too much, I thought. But ever since I had been in Africa, Bill, Carl's old gun-boy had been talking of "Memsahib's lion"—the lion I would some day get for our collection; and my husband, too, had referred to it from time to time. And now Carl, on the first day he had felt justified in taking wholly for our own personal enjoyment, had announced that we would go down into "Bill's country"—a region which this extraordinary native had investigated for himself and which, he stated, afforded many more lions than we had elsewhere seen. Apparently I would have to begin that serious business of hunting a lion.

We had started shortly after dawn. Fold after fold, the hazy curtain of the morning was lifted high above the rosy veldt. From every tree bright-colored birds raised their voices in a joyous matin song. We shivered a little in our sweaters as

130

the wind blew about us sharp and cold. For miles we traveled steadily toward a fringe of blue and distant hills and as we reached the first low-lying knolls we saw several lions and were conscious of others, just mere spots of dull gold in the brighter grass—spots that looked out at us for a brief second with steady shining eyes and then faded utterly into the obscurity whence they had come. We overtook another lion a few yards from his abandoned kill. He was sitting on his haunches in the grass, watching us boldly before starting up toward the shade of some dense vegetation on the ridge above. We surprised and scattered a band of snarling hyenas and a flock of vultures quarreling together over the fragments of the feast. The lion took a good look at us as he sat, next he rose and looked at us again. Then turning slowly he walked leisurely with the greatest dignity and composure to the thick bush above. Though our course led somewhat along his path, yet not once did he deign to turn and look in our direction, nor did he in the slightest quicken his pace as he approached the shelter of the ridge.

As we traveled on we came to a wide valley where all the creatures of the veldt had foregathered in parade. Impala and eland, monkeys and baboons, parrots and parakeets, hartebeest and wildebeest, zebra and giraffe, topi and gazelles were feeding there. We had been watching a fine herd of giraffe. They were the leaf-patterned giraffe, tall and stately creatures, beautifully marked in brown and reddish tan with indefinite patterns resembling in design and color the foliage of the oak in autumn. Here we found them far more numerous than their more vividly marked brothers of the north, the reticulated giraffe.

Now the giraffe family was in friendly mood. They stared at us. The young ones, taking refuge behind the grown-ups,

131

played hide and seek and ran and frisked about. They bit and licked each other and pranced jauntily up and down, happy and unconcerned as only the young of all things, man or beast, are wont to be. Then two hungry twins, apparently but a few weeks old, cantered toward us right in the open where their mother stood. They informed her they were ready for their second breakfast. On either side of the watchful female they fed until they had their fill. They appeared wholly heedless of our presence and were certainly without concern.

We stayed a long time beside the giraffe herd. They were frankly curious and showed not the slightest trace of fear. We disliked to move and by so doing cause them to stampede.

But finally we started on as the sun was now both high and hot. Suddenly my husband's attention was attracted by something two hundred yards away across the valley. A thick growth of shrubbery outlined a deep gully—a donga where the water ran abundantly in the rainy season. Between us and the watercourse great heat waves rolled up, changing both the size and contour of every object. "They may be only Tommies," my husband said as he gazed at several dark objects half concealed in the thin fringe of grass, "but I think they are lions." Carl, who was taking his turn at driving the car, now drove nearer and stopped for a better view. Here there was no question as to the identity of the animals. Three big lions were sitting up on their haunches watching us intently. In a moment two other tawny cats walked up a few yards away. They too sat down in a direct line with the others. Then suddenly from out the dark green bush a very large chocolate-colored lioness came into full view. She did not loiter with the others. Quickly passing through the scattered scrub and thinning grass, she walked boldly out into the open. A recent grass fire had here burned a large swath and when she reached the burn she lifted her feet high and stepped out gingerly on the harsh stubble, as though it was none too kind to her padded paws. But she did not once hesitate, so intent was she on seeing who we were. Carl now held his big elephant gun on her, while I seized my Goerz and photographed her as rapidly as I could turn my film. It was a crime that Carl could not move back to where his motion picture camera was mounted and there make the photographs that would tell the whole story.

The lioness was now about fifty yards away. When she reached a little green thorn bush not more than three feet high and as slender as a cane, she began to stalk us with lowered head. She came on slowly, her head lower than her shoulders, her body stretched almost to the ground, for all the world as a cat lengthens out its body when it stalks a bird. Before she left the flimsy shelter of this bush she turned every now and then to look back at the other lions, doubtless to see if they were

133

coming too. Then she came out quite away from the little bush, and with head still held low glided up toward a tree nearer to us and to her right. Here she sat down to one side and back of the tree and gave us a long "once over." But this view of us was not satisfactory. The big lioness got up and deliberately began her stalk again. She had our wind. She was intent on knowing who we were. She reached the tree. She walked to the other side of it. She came straight toward us. Not once did she take her eyes off us; not once did she hesitate. I was profoundly thrilled—throbbing with excitement. So utterly fascinated was I by the big determined beast and so completely did I rely upon my husband's ability to protect me, I would have sat there without moving until the great cat reached our car. "If she comes five steps nearer I'll have to shoot," Carl said in his low cool voice. "Oh, please let her come a little nearer," I whispered. But Carl paid no attention to my foolish request. With his gun on her he tooted the motor horn but she gave no heed. Then he started the noisy engine. The lioness came a step nearer and I photographed. Finally both Carl and Bill began to shout at the top of their lungs. She stopped and gazed straight at us for twenty full seconds. Then as leisurely, de-

134

liberately and gracefully as she had come across the open veldt toward us, and as only a lion can, she walked with slow and measured pace back to the edge of the gully where her five companions still waited for her. In a moment they had all vanished in the donga.

It took ten minutes for us to breathe normally again. "Oh, how glad I am I didn't have to kill that beautiful big cat," Carl said, "but I gave her only two more steps; then I would have been compelled to shoot."

He paced it off. The lioness had turned at exactly *thirty paces*!

"You have seen one of the greatest sights anyone will ever see in Africa," my husband told me. Of that I was convinced past any doubt. This intrepid lioness had shown a most superb courage and audacity. Though supported by her five ready companions a few rods away, yet she had ventured to come out alone to investigate another living creature ten times her size, as we and our motor car were to her. Undaunted she had dared to challenge a creature with limitless powers of danger for her, had she but known. It was indeed one of the rare experiences of Africa whose memory will never fade.

135

THE Belgian Congo is the only country in Africa that has made an attempt to domesticate or train elephants. You can hear any number of opinions as to whether the African elephant *can* be domesticated, or at least trusted after it has been tamed, but Colonel Offermann had no doubt about it.

"The African elephant isn't a pet and it isn't a toy, but as a working elephant it will meet any test," he told me. "The important thing is to train the men who will handle the elephants. With well-trained men you can get exactly the same results that you get from an Asiatic elephant."

Colonel Offermann had been director of the station for sixteen years and although he had moved on to the post of chief game warden he still had a great affection for elephants. He talked about elephants all the way across the northeastern corner of the Congo as we drove, in a rented automobile, from Aba to Dungu and

Journey for Elephants

BY WILLIAM BRIDGES

Photographs by Henry Goldstein

Faradje and eventually to the station at Gangala-na-Bodio. It was a rolling country of tall grass and scrub trees. Here and there the bushes along the road had been broken or uprooted and the bank trampled; a party of elephants had crossed the road during the night. Word had been passed on to Colonel Offermann at Aba that elephants were persistently raiding a mission garden somewhere along the line and he wanted to look into the report, for pressure was sure to be brought on him to allow the elephants to be shot.

136

We found the mission and stopped to inquire. Yes, elephants had raided the garden once, but that was more than a month before. They had been seen a few times since, but the mission boys scared them off by banging on sheets of tin.

"Well, I'm glad I caught up with that one," the game warden commented. "Now I'll be ready when I get a report that these elephants are destroying every garden in the region. It's usually like that—the stories are exaggerated."

As we drove down the long tree-bordered avenue leading to the station, the elephants were just returning from their afternoon bath in the flooded Dungu River. For an instant no *cornacs* were in sight and the elephants, to all intents and purposes, were completely free and wild. No zoo bars, no chains, no prodding attendants—just elephants in an African landscape, with the hot yellow sun slanting down through the mimosas and gilding their backs.

After dinner we sat on the veranda in the warm darkness and talked about elephants. Colonel Offermann had worked out the technique they now use for capturing elephants. In the early years of the domestication service a party of Indian elephant men was brought into the Congo to show the Belgians how they made captures in India, but the *Keddah*, or corral, method of India was never very successful, and Colonel Offermann's system has been used for many years. It depends pretty much on the sheer stamina of the hunters. The hunting party always consists of a European mounted on a swift Sudanese pony, a team of 16 to 18 men afoot, a party of 10 to 15 monitor elephants and their caretakers, and an echelon of carriers or wagons with camping equipment, food, ammunition, spare ropes, and the like.

Four of the actual hunters carry guns; the others are equipped with lassos of soft rope. All are volunteers and all

137

are Azande tribesmen—tall, thin, long-legged, and born hunters, intensely proud of their jobs and the military discipline of the station. On the trail they do not talk much, Colonel Offermann said. They just watch the track and keep going tirelessly.

The station hunts by special permission in the Garamba National Park, which lies just across the Dungu River, and occasionally in the bush and grassland outside the park. The Garamba is an immense area of 4700 square miles that runs right up to the Sudan border. It is mostly low bush and tall grass—superb elephant country.

Theoretically, nobody is allowed to burn off the grass in the Congo, but actually most of central Africa is ablaze during the dry season, when the Garamba Park regularly gets burned, starting when the rains slacken in December. By the end of January the terrain is mostly clear and the elephants gather in

big herds, sometimes numbering hundreds of animals, an amalgamation of the smaller family groups of a dozen to fifty that wander together during the rainy season.

The first two weeks in February, consequently, are the best time to capture elephants. The big herds find shelter and food during the daytime in patches of unburned bush and at night they drift into the burned places, because there the grass is coming up and is fresh and tender. By daybreak they are usually back in the unburned bush.

Unsuspicious feeding elephants leave a hurricane path of trampled bush and broken branches, tusk-scarred earth and droppings behind them and are easy enough to follow. The rolling terrain and the clumps of bush and grass make it easy for the hunters to approach a herd, often within a few hundred feet. Their approach is always from downwind, of course.

139

From the shelter of trees or a hill the hunters size up the herd, silently sorting out with their eyes the young bulls and the cows with young, which are most likely to cause trouble. Some youngster ten or twelve years old, around six feet tall, may be close at hand; if so, a few whispered words determine that he will be the first catch.

"The moment before attack is something you never forget," Colonel Offermann said. "It is like war, the moment before a cavalry charge. You check every man with your eyes; they are all coiled springs, ready to leap forward. They don't say anything and neither do you; you don't need to speak, for each of you has confidence in the other.

"Your eyes rest last on the chief hunter. He nods. You flick your finger, and the riflemen fire in the air. At that instant the whole team leaps forward and breaks cover, yelling and screeching and running toward the herd."

Naturally, the frightened herd stampedes, and the hunters go whooping after them. The youngster they have settled on in advance may lumber off at right angles, he may swerve into the heart of the herd—he is unpredictable. If he stays reasonably clear, his fate is sealed. The swiftest and most skillful hunter draws alongside him and makes contact—literally grabbing the elephant by the tail sometimes. With luck the hunter may quickly cast a loop of rope around a hind foot; all the hunters are incredibly dextrous at this dangerous maneuver of roping the foot of a fast-running elephant.

The first contact is a signal for the whole team to pile on. More ropes are cast; some stick and some slip off. The yelling, leaping hunters are all around the elephant except within range of his tusks. They hang on to the ropes and slow his run, snubbing him against every bush or tree, whooping after him if the bush is uprooted and he breaks free. Another leg and then another is roped, and the pulling begins in all directions.

140

The sheer weight of men slows the animal. Sooner or later a snub holds; momentarily the youngster is stopped in his mad course, and in a few seconds he is swathed in ropes like a kitten in a skein of yarn. He is the hunt's first capture, and an easy one.

They are not all so easy and uncomplicated. Young bulls and cows with calves are always the dangerous members of the herd. The old bulls and old cows simply run away, but a mother cow may get the idea that she has to protect her calf, even though the hunters have no designs on it, and will tuck her trunk under her head and charge. Or a callow bull, liking trouble for its own sake, will abandon flight and give battle. Sometimes the hunters can frighten the attacker away by firing in the air; as a last resort they shoot the charging elephant.

Actually, snubbing a capture down, stopping it completely, is a cooperative business, of course, but the hunter who casts the first rope around an elephant—and makes it stick, is officially credited with the capture and often the elephant is named for him. One Zande boy named Kalisue was credited with 32 captures in 14 years.

As soon as an elephant is captured, a runner goes back to the base and brings up a monitor elephant. Generally this old, tame elephant towers over the newly captured one and dominates it in size and strength. In any event, the monitor is trained and obedient and it takes but a few moments for it to range alongside and for the ropes to be cast off and then recast to lash the two elephants together, the youngster tethered around the neck. Wild elephants are not always completely calmed and comforted by the presence of the monitor but, if they turn fractious, the monitors quickly cool them off with a swipe of the trunk or tusks. Generally there is very little trouble once the monitors are put in charge.

The training of a wild elephant starts in a mild way at the

base camp of the hunting party, where it gets accustomed to the presence of men and to being tied to its monitor. Generally, one man is assigned to each elephant and carries through its entire training. He works on the principle of gaining the elephant's confidence, talking to it continuously, singing to it, and at certain stages of its education, stroking it for hours with leafy branches.

The elephants get accustomed to song almost as much as to speech: the fierce, proud victory song, *Lala-li-soi,* that the hunters sing around the captives when the hunt is over and they are all gathered at the base; the *Dina-dina* marching song to reassure the elephants as they are approaching the station or a new camp; and the other nameless and almost wordless chants that are repetitious and therefore soothing to the animals. There are songs that are special to the stroking of an elephant with branches, to crossing a river, to marching, to entering a post. Some of them are corruptions of the songs of

the Indian elephant men of long ago, but mostly they are pure African.

Training starts in earnest in the "lines" at the station. These are two parallel rows of iron stakes set in a red brick pavement in the center of the station. There are stakes for nearly a hundred elephants and in some seasons they are all occupied. The new elephants are assigned to definite spots and are staked down with soft ropes, either by all four feet or by the right front foot and left hind foot. The ropes are sufficiently slack so that the elephant has all necessary freedom of movement, but not enough to let it encroach on its neighbor's area. The lines, completely open except for the low brick wall behind each row of stakes, are actually the stables for the station's herd. The elephants are tied up there at night or when they are not feeding

143

in the bush or being trained in the training square at the end of the lines.

After a week or two of rest in the lines the new elephants have generally lost some of their first nervousness and are ready for training. A *cornac* rides up alongside on a monitor; a rope is passed around one youngster's neck, drawing it close to the monitor. Another trainee is attached to the other side. Then the feet of the new elephants are loosened and they go for a walk with the monitor. A *cornac* rides the monitor, of course, and the little party promenades and feeds in the bush near the station for several hours each day.

The next step is to get the elephant accustomed to a rider on its back—a longer and more difficult step. For a few days the *cornacs* gather around each elephant and chant *Lala-li-soi* in unison, stroking it gently with branches and tossing it bananas, sweet potatoes, pineapples, stalks of sugar cane—all delicacies that the elephants like. This soothing goes on for days, a few minutes at a time at first, then for a quarter of an hour morning and evening. Finally the morning comes when a *cornac* makes the first leap onto a new elephant's back. There is generally a violent protest on the elephant's part and the *cornac* is lucky if he stays on even a few minutes. The next morning he leaps on again, and in a few days all but the most recalcitrant elephants accept their riders as a matter of course. But it may take months for some stubborn animals.

After two months the elephants are taught to get down and get up at command. While the *cornacs* keep up a running fire of soothing talk and the command *"Saba! Saba!"* (Steady! Steady!), the young elephants are tied with short ropes that bring them down on their knees. By this time an elephant is used to the man on its back and when he urges, *"Kulala! Kulala! Kulala!"* (Lie down!) and tugs at the rope around its

144

legs, the pressure, the tugging and the command all induce it to go completely down. Once it touches the ground, the ropes are slacked off and it rises. Then it is rewarded with a piece of sugar cane. In five or six days most young elephants learn to obey the "Kulala!" command readily and learn that *"Kulungula!"* means "Get up!"

There are several other phases of the training: the monotonous period when the *cornac,* with purely African patience, repeats *dre-dre-dre* for hours while teaching the elephant to pick up a ball of grass and hand it to him with its trunk; the months when the newcomers march around and around by the side of their monitors; the stage when they are teamed up with other young elephants of the previous year, and the high school student, as it were, instructs the primary class. This stage is usually reached about eight months after capture. Soon the more docile youngsters are allowed to go to the feeding grounds attached to the monitor only by a loose single cord around the neck, and finally even this is removed.

Within six to eight months after capture, most elephants are fully indoctrinated and can be given their liberty. They follow the monitor readily with or without *cornacs* on their backs. They are members of the family and can be trusted—within reason.

EVEN though whales live in the water, they are not fish; they are mammals. Mammals have warm blood that remains at the same temperature all the time. The blood of a fish is "cold" and changes with the temperature of the water. Mammals breathe air with lungs. Fish breathe oxygen in the water by means of gills. The young of fish are hatched from eggs. The young of mammals are born alive and nursed with milk. A whale's milk is white and looks just like cow's milk.

The great, many times great, grandfathers of whales lived on land. That was fifty or sixty million years ago. No one knows just how long. But we do know they are one of the oldest groups of mammals. When they lived on land, they had bodies like other mammals. They were covered with hair, walked on four legs and had ears on the outside of their heads.

For some reason the ancestors of whales left the land and took up life in the water. We can only guess *why* they did that. But we can see *how* it was done if we

The Land Animal That Went to Sea

BY ROY CHAPMAN ANDREWS

Illustrated by Thomas W. Voter

look at a seal. The ancestors of seals used to be entirely land mammals, but many years ago they began to spend more and more time in the water. Now they only come out on the shore to give birth to their young and to sleep in the sun. Their bodies have changed a great deal to fit them for life in the water. After a few more million years they will undoubtedly become

146

as fishlike in shape as whales and never come on land. Whales must have gone through the same stages that seals are going through.

Nature did an amazing job in adapting a whale to live in the water. One would never think it was possible. Everything about the body, inside and out, had to be changed. It was a very, very, very slow process. Millions of years passed before the change was complete. To be able to move through the water easily, the body must be long and slender. So in each generation of the ancestral whales, the body grew to be more and more like that of a fish.

Any part of an animal that isn't being used disappears eventually. That is why whales have no external ears. Outside ears help a land mammal to collect the sound waves that pass through the air. You have often seen a partly deaf man put

his hand behind his ear to help him hear. But water carries sound much better than air. Therefore, outside ears are not necessary to a whale or any other animal that lives in the water. A whale's ears show only as a tiny hole on each side of the head behind the eye. But the muscles that used to control the outside ears are still there under the skin. So we know whales once had external ears. The ears of seals are tiny and are gradually disappearing. In generation after generation the ears get smaller as the animals spend more and more time in the water and less on land.

Nature had to make an extraordinary change in the way a whale breathes. Because it is a mammal, a whale must hold its breath below the water's surface just like a person. If it didn't, it would drown.

A whale must breathe as soon as possible when it comes up from a long dive. So Nature moved the nostrils backward and up to the very top of the head. Thus the nose is the first part of the body to appear when the whale rises to the surface.

As soon as a whale reaches the surface, it opens its nostrils. These have been closed as tight as a trap door. The whale blows out its breath in a great *whoosh*. The breath has become hot from staying in the lungs for such a long time. Also it is saturated with water vapor.

When it strikes the cool outer air, it condenses and forms a column of vapor. You can do the same thing on a cold winter day when you "see your breath." The whale's vapor column shoots up fifteen or twenty feet. Whalemen called it the "spout."

People used to believe that whales took water in through the mouth and spouted it out through the nose. A whale could not do that because of another adaptation that Nature has made. The nasal passages do not open into the back of the

148

mouth as in a land mammal. Instead they are directly connected with the lungs. This is by means of an extension of the windpipe, called the "epiglottis." It fits into the soft passage between the nostrils and the lungs. It entirely shuts off the nasal tubes from the mouth. Thus the whale can swallow its food beneath the surface without getting water in its lungs. But it can't breathe through its mouth.

When whales began to live entirely in the water, Nature had to provide some way to keep them warm. A fish doesn't have to worry about that, for when it is cold the blood temperature of a fish drops. In warm water it rises. But a mammal's blood always remains at the same temperature. A dog or a cat or a bear grows longer and thicker hair in the winter. That prevents the body heat from being absorbed by the cold air. People do the same thing by putting on more clothes.

Nature solved the problem of keeping the whale warm by developing a thick layer of fat, called "blubber," between the skin and the flesh. Fat makes a very warm blanket. Whales that live in the cold Arctic seas have very thick blubber. The blubber of those species that inhabit temperate or tropical waters is comparatively thin.

Seals have blubber too. It is not very thick since they also have fur or hair. That is because they live partly on land. After some millions of years, when they come to spend all their time in the water, the hair will vanish. Then the blubber will be much thicker. The walrus of the Arctic Ocean has thick blubber and its hair is thin.

Besides giving warmth to a land mammal, hair acts as a protection for its skin. But a whale doesn't need hair for that purpose even though its skin is very soft and thin. Because it lives in the water, it doesn't have to worry about thorns or bushes or rocks which might tear its skin. A big whale has skin

149

only half of an inch thick. It is perfectly dry and has no oil or sweat glands. They proved to be unnecessary, so over a period of time they disappeared.

When whales took to the water, they had to have some way of swimming well. Thus the back part of the body expanded. It became the wide, flat, boneless tail, or "flukes." The tail of a fish is vertical, but the flukes of a whale are horizontal. The flukes help the whale to rise to the surface quickly.

The legs of a land mammal are not wide or flat enough for good swimming. So the bones and fingers of the whale's fore-legs grew together. After a while they became covered with connective tissue and blubber. These make very fine paddles. They help in rapid turning and in balancing while the flukes push the whale forward. Because the hind legs weren't of much use, they became shorter with each generation. After millions of years they disappeared entirely. In living whales the only remnants of these hind legs are small chunks of bone buried deep in the flesh.

150

The changes that had to be made inside the whale are just as remarkable as those on the outside. The entire skeleton is loosely put together. Thus the animal's body is very flexible and has great freedom of movement for swimming. To support the big head, the bones of the neck are shortened and packed close together. The breastbone is very small. The ribs are so loosely joined to the backbone that the lungs can be completely filled with air.

Whales are the biggest animals that ever lived. Why can they grow so large? It is because the water supports their bodies. If a land animal gets too big, its legs can't hold it up and it is unable to move about. If a bird is too heavy, it cannot fly. But there is no limit to the size a whale can grow since water supports it.

151

For this same reason the young whales are very large at birth. I saw a new-born sulphur-bottom whale that was twenty-five feet long. Its mother measured eighty feet. The baby weighed about 16,000 pounds. A land mammal could not carry babies of such size.

All whales live in oceans. Most of the porpoises do, too, except for one group found in the Ganges River, the Orinoco River, and the Tungting Lake of China.

No example of evolution is more wonderful than that of whales. But it must be remembered that this extraordinary change from a land to a water mammal was very slow. In each generation the body structure was altered a little more to fit the new life. It took millions of years to produce a whale as we see it now.

IF ever you should go by chance
    To jungles in the East,
And if there should to you advance
    A large and tawny beast,
If he roars at you as you're dyin'
You'll know it is the Asian Lion.

Or if sometime when roaming round,
    A noble wild beast greets you,
With black stripes on a yellow ground,
    Just notice if he eats you.
This simple rule may help you learn
The Bengal Tiger to discern.

How to Tell the Wild Animals

BY CAROLYN WELLS

Illustrated by Maurice Sendak

If strolling forth,
    a beast you view,
      Whose hide with spots
        is peppered,
As soon as he has lept on you,
    You'll know it is a Leopard.
'Twill do no good
    to roar with pain,
He'll only lep and lep again.

If when you're walking round your yard,
    You meet a creature there,
Who hugs you very, very hard,
    Be sure it is the Bear.
If you have any doubt, I guess
He'll give you just one more caress.

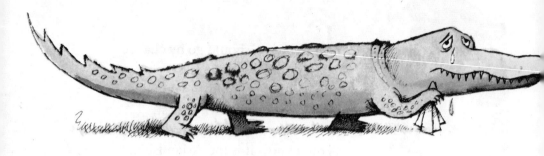

Though to distinguish beasts of prey
    A novice might nonplus,
The Crocodiles you always may
    Tell from Hyenas thus:
Hyenas come with merry smiles;
But if they weep, they're Crocodiles.

The true Chameleon is small,
    A lizard sort of thing;
He hasn't any ears at all,
    And not a single wing.
If there is nothing in the tree,
'Tis the Chameleon you see.

The Panther

BY OGDEN NASH

THE panther is like a leopard,
Except it hasn't been peppered.
Should you behold a panther crouch,
Prepare to say Ouch.
Better yet, if called by a panther,
Don't anther.

Illustrated by
Maurice Sendak

The Lama

BY OGDEN NASH

THE one-l lama,
He's a priest;
The two-l llama,
He's a beast.
And I will bet
A silk pajama
There isn't any
Three-l lllama

155

The Vulture

BY HILAIRE BELLOC

THE Vulture eats between his meals,
    And that's the reason why
He very, very rarely feels
    As well as you and I.

His eye is dull, his head is bald,
    His neck is growing thinner.
Oh! What a lesson for us all
    To only eat at dinner!

The Ostrich Is A Silly Bird

BY MARY E. W. FREEMAN

Illustrated by
Ervine Metzel

THE ostrich is a silly bird,
    With scarcely any mind.
He often runs so very fast,
    He leaves himself behind.

And when he gets there, has to stand
    And hang about till night,
Without a blessed thing to do
    Until he comes in sight.   156

Habits of the Hippopotamus

BY ARTHUR GUITERMAN

Illustrated by
Ervine Metzel

THE hippopotamus is strong
    And huge of head and broad of bustle;
The limbs on which he rolls along
    Are big with hippopotomuscle.

He does not greatly care for sweets
    Like ice cream, apple pie, or custard,
But takes to flavor what he eats
    A little hippopotomustard.

The hippopotamus is true
    To all his principles, and just;
He always tries his best to do
    The things one hippopotomust.

He never rides in trucks or trams,
    In taxicabs or omnibuses,
And so keeps out of traffic jams
    And other hippopotomusses.

Circus Elephant

BY KATHRYN WORTH

Illustrated by Clare Leighton

Does the elephant remember
In gray light before the dawn,
Old noises of the jungle
In mornings past and gone?

Does the elephant remember
The cry of hungry beasts;
The tiger and the leopard,
The lion at his feast?

Do his mighty eardrums listen
For the thunder of the feet
Of the buffalo and zebra
In the dark and dreadful heat?

Does his majesty remember
Does he stir himself and dream
Of the long forgotten music
Of a long forgotten stream?

Now this is the Law of the Jungle—
 as old and as true as the sky;
And the Wolf that shall keep it may prosper,
 but the Wolf that shall break it must die.

As the creeper that girdles the tree-trunk
 the Law runneth forward and back—
For the strength of the Pack is the Wolf,
 and the strength of the Wolf is the Pack.

Wash daily from nose-tip to tail-tip;
 drink deeply,
  but never too deep;
And remember the night is for
 hunting, and forget not
  the day is for sleep.

The Jackal may follow the Tiger,
 but, Cub, when
  thy whiskers are grown,
Remember the Wolf is a hunter—
 go forth and get food of thine own.

The Law of the Jungle

BY RUDYARD KIPLING

*Illustrated by
Emma Landau*

Keep peace with the Lords of the Jungle—the Tiger,
 the Panther, the Bear;
And trouble not Hathi the Silent, and mock not the
 Boar in his lair.

When Pack meets with Pack in the Jungle, and
 neither will go from the trail,
Lie down till the leaders have spoken—it may
 be fair words shall prevail.

159

When ye fight with a Wolf of the Pack, ye must
    fight him alone and afar,
Lest others take part in the quarrel, and the
    Pack be diminished by war.

The Lair of the Wolf is his refuge, and where
    he has made him his home,
Not even the Head Wolf may enter, not even the
    Council may come.

If ye kill before midnight, be silent, and wake
    not the woods with your bay,
Lest ye frighten the deer from the crops, and
    the brothers go empty away.

Ye may kill for yourselves, and your mates, and
    your cubs as they need, and ye can;
But kill not for pleasure of killing, and seven
    times never kill Man.

If ye plunder his Kill from a weaker, devour not
    all in thy pride;
Pack-Right is the right of the meanest; so leave
    him the head and the hide.

The Kill of the Pack is the meat of the Pack.
    Ye must eat where it lies;
And no one may carry away of that meat to his
    lair, or he dies.

Because of his age and his cunning, because of
his gripe and his paw,
In all that the Law leaveth open, the word of
the Head Wolf is Law.

Now these are the Laws of the Jungle, and many
and mighty are they;
But the head and the hoof of the Law and the
haunch and the hump is—Obey!

ONCE upon a time, not so very long ago, wildlife in wonderful variety lived almost everywhere in America. In the forests of the East there were deer, elk, bear, and even buffalo. There were grouse, wild turkeys, passenger pigeons, and ivory-billed woodpeckers. In the north woods there were timber wolves and lynxes, bobcats, martens, fishers, and wolverines. Along the streams lived raccoons, beaver, mink, and otter. To the west, on our prairies and plains, roamed vast herds of antelope and buffalo, besides coyotes, badgers, prairie chickens, sage grouse, sharptails, and jack rabbits. In the mountains of the Far West there were mountain goats, mountain sheep, grizzly bears, ptarmigans, and the great California condors.

Some of these wild creatures were present in numbers almost beyond belief. Scientists estimate that there were 60 million buffalo and as many beaver, 2 million wolves, 40 million antelope, 10 million elk, perhaps half a million black bears, and countless millions of passenger pigeons. No one knows these figures exactly, of course. But we do know that some of these wild creatures are gone forever, and that nearly all of them are far less common than they used to be.

The Story of Wildlife Conservation

BY EDWARD H. GRAHAM AND WILLIAM R. VAN DERSAL

Illustrated by Robert Frankenberg

Since our ancestors came to this country, we have changed the face of America. We cut down most of the forests, plowed

162

the prairies, pastured cattle and sheep on the plains, and drained the marshes and swamps. These things we did to make homes for ourselves and become a great nation. What we did changed our wildlife as well as our land. The variety and abundance of our wildlife today are different from what they were in primitive times. The fate of the wild creatures we shall have with us in the years to come will be determined by the way we treat them. It will depend on what we do with the farms, ranches, forests, marshes, and waters in which they live.

The first American game law was passed one hundred years before the Declaration of Independence, when Connecticut made it unlawful to kill game at certain seasons of the year. Before we became a nation, deer, ruffed grouse, quail, wild turkey, and heath hen were protected by various states. Protection did not save some of our wild creatures. The heath hen disappeared. Other protected species have become greatly reduced in numbers.

We have hundreds of laws about wildlife. Some prohibit hunting when wildlife is nesting or caring for its young. Others limit the number of quail, or rabbits, or other kind of wildlife that you may shoot in a single day or season. Laws tell when you may fish, how many fish you may catch, and how big they must be. Automatic shotguns and gun silencers are generally outlawed. Laws regulate payment for damages by wildlife, as when deer eat farm crops. Many other laws are designed to control game of all sorts.

Not all wildlife laws relate to game—animals hunted for sport. It is illegal to sell feathers, quills, plumes, and other parts of wild birds. At one time the magnificent snowy egret was nearly exterminated because people killed it to get its beautiful delicate plumes for trimming women's hats. This splendid bird is plentiful now because laws were passed to protect it.

163

Ever since Massachusetts in 1818 passed the first law to protect a non-game bird, the robin, we have given more and more protection to all kinds of wildlife. We protect all songbirds. We even prize game birds in some places for their insect-eating value. In Ohio, for example, the bobwhite quail is protected by law throughout the year. Probably no other country in the world defends its wildlife as well as we do.

Our first national wildlife refuge was a little sandy island off the coast of Florida. Theodore Roosevelt was President then, and in 1903 he designated Pelican Island as a protected area for a colony of brown pelicans. The island was about five acres in extent, which was a pretty small beginning. The warden there was paid at first by a scientific society—The American Ornithologists' Union. Later our government took it over, warden, salary, and all.

Even though it was tiny, Pelican Island was the beginning of our great national refuge system. Today this system includes 18 million acres. There are state refuges, too, that include about 50 million acres inside their boundaries.

164

Today we have many sanctuaries scattered along our coasts. There is the Great White Heron Refuge in the Florida Keys. There is the Breton Island Refuge off the Mississippi Delta. Three Arch Capes off the Oregon coast is famous. So is the Farallon Refuge near the mouth of San Francisco Bay.

Island refuges like these are important to herons, terns, gulls, cormorants, pelicans, egrets, ibises—especially on our eastern and southern shores. On our western island refuges, the birds include murres, puffins, auklets, petrels, guillemots, and cormorants. Most of these birds are strange to anyone who has not lived near the sea. Yet the islands harbor many more kinds of wildlife than these. Ducks and geese, numerous water and shore birds, and many mammals are common.

Northward, along the Alaskan coast, clear out into the Aleutian Islands, our chain of refuges is continued. The vast numbers of colony-nesting birds on them are said to dwarf the numbers we see in the States. These islands are useful also and very important for seals, sea lions, sea otters, fur seals, walruses, and dozens of other interesting types of wildlife.

WHEN I was eight years old I kept a Natural History Museum in my mother's linen closet. It was probably the only museum of its kind in the world. It had birds' nests and sea shells and fossils and pressed leaves and skulls of cows and dogs and the things that a regular museum does have. Of course it did not have as many things as the regular ones have; but it had just as many departments.

Then, too, some of the exhibits were a little doubtful. I mean by that there were pieces of flint, for instance, that *might* have been Indian arrowheads at some time, or Early Britons' battle-axes. And there were pieces of bone that *could* have been ribs from a dinosaur. However, on the description cards of all those exhibits that I wasn't sure about I would put a question mark after the title—like this:

My Private Natural History Museum

BY HUGH LOFTING

Illustrated by Susan Perl

PREHISTORIC FRYING PAN
(?)
(*Discovered in the Jones's Backyard*)
VERY SCARCE. PROBABLY MADE OF GOLD. (??)

Two question marks meant that the information was especially doubtful. My museum specialized in Natural Curiosities. Anything that was odd—queerly shaped stones; roots that looked like old men's faces; sticks, so worm-eaten that they looked like Chinese carving; anything that mystified me or seemed as though it should have a history to it—such treasures were kept in a special case in my museum. And my imagination had a perfectly wonderful time spinning yarns over all the strange adventures these objects might have gone through.

On the door of the linen closet there was a sign that read: "THE MUSEUM IS OPEN TO THE PUBLIC ON WEEK DAYS FROM 9 A.M. TILL 5 P.M. AND ON SUNDAYS FROM 11 A.M. TILL 5 P.M." You see I didn't get up so early on Sundays. The public didn't come in very large numbers— mostly my brothers, our cat, and our dog. And when they had seen the museum every day for a week, I couldn't persuade them to come any more. So after that, whenever I wanted to play "Museum" I had to pay the public to visit the show. I usually paid them with marbles or lollipops. I was a very public-spirited Museum Director.

And not only was I the Director; I was the Chairman, the Curator, and the whole staff of Naturalists. The thing I most enjoyed in the business was collecting the specimens for the museum. One day I'd be ornithologist and would go round the countryside, cutting down last year's birds' nests together with the piece of tree or bush they were built on. Other days I'd be a geologist, collecting fossils and different kinds of rocks. And sometimes a botanist, hunting flower and leaf specimens. And every Saturday night I was an astronomer, looking for falling stars through my father's opera glasses. (I saw a number fall, but I never found where they fell—and consequently my museum was somewhat short on meteorites.)

But if the public was not very keen on visiting my museum, the rats and mice were. They thought my museum was a lovely place. They liked my collection so well they even took parts of it away with them. For instance, they took the old birds' nests—to make over into new ones for themselves. Of course the rats and the mice didn't come to the Museum in the regular visiting hours, from nine to five. They came in the middle of the night.

Well, when my parents found out that my museum in the linen closet was so popular with the rats and mice, they thought that it ought to be closed to the public for the spring—for the spring-cleaning in fact. And when they discovered to what extent the rats and mice had made themselves at home in the Ornithological Department, they refused to allow the museum to be reopened in their house any more.

One of the stories that my mother tells about this period of my career as a naturalist is that I used to bring home the old skulls of dogs and cats that I found under the hedges and boil them, to get them clean and white for my museum, in her best saucepan! It isn't true. I used her second-best one. It was bigger.

So that was the end of my Private Natural History Museum. It was never reopened to the public (although I had already laid the foundation stone with great ceremony at the bottom of the garden for a brand new building), because that summer I went away to boarding-school. But I often look back upon it with pride. It was certainly the only museum of its kind in the world.

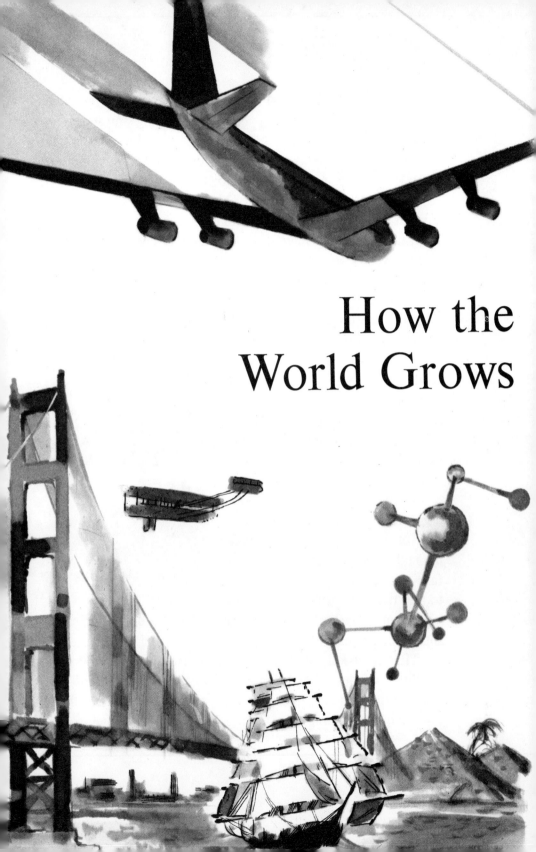

How the
World Grows

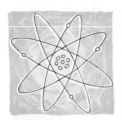

FROM the very beginning of recorded time, there have been strange mysteries in the earth. The lightning tearing its crooked paths down the summer sky; the luminous ribbons of the Northern Lights waving across the polar dark; St. Elmo's fire, playing around the masts of ships at sea—all these were fearful mysteries. Less obvious, but as strange, were the magnet stone that could give "life" to iron, and the yellow amber that attracted feathers and bits of straw when it was rubbed. People noticed these phenomena often; no one could guess there was any connection among them.

The substance of the earth itself was another mystery. What was the earth made of? Were earth and air and water made of fire, as some of the Greeks thought in the early days? Or did they all come from water? Or were they nothing at all but the imagination of men? No one could tell.

And finally there was the mystery of light—a mystery hardly noticed since it seemed so natural to watch day following night, to feel the light of the sun, to see it warming the cherry trees to a drift of white blossoms in the spring, or ripening the grain in the summer fields.

The Scientists and the Bright Design

BY
KATHERINE B. SHIPPEN

Illustrated by
Charles M. Daugherty

That electricity and magnetism, the atoms made of tiny moving particles, and the moving radiant light, were all one energy, all manifestations of the cosmic fire—this was a truth that men were a long time finding out. For it was much easier to imagine that these things were supernatural in their essence than that they had a common scientific cause.

Whenever fearful things are little understood they have been said to be the work of spirits. Many thought the magnet stones were "full of gods," and they spoke of the "soul" of the amber. Countless were the legends of how the earth was made: the Hebrews, for example, thought that it was dust, fashioned by the hand of God. In Persia, in Peru, in China, and in Egypt, and in many other places, the sun was worshipped. Men called it the giver of life, the god who was the glory of all created things.

But there have always been some men who are not content with legend and poetry, those who want to examine and compare, to find out the laws that underlie life and all material things. These men are the scientists. Thales of Miletus was one of the first of them. He lived in Greece in the sixth century before Christ. It was Thales, apparently, who first tried to study the "magic power" of amber, and who said he thought that water was the "elemental fluid." He was an astronomer also, and watched the skies so long and so carefully that he was at length able to predict an eclipse—an achievement which won him a great reputation. The citizens of Miletus erected a statue to this early scientist. They inscribed it: "Miletus, fairest of Ionian cities, gave birth to Thales, great astronomer, wisest of mortals in all kinds of knowledge."

But the centuries passed, and what Thales had done was half forgotten. In the first century before Christ, Lucretius, the Roman, wrote his long poem *On the Nature of Things*. In it he tried to bring together the scientific facts that had been revealed up to his time. But his poem, too, was forgotten, and not until the thirteenth century in Europe did Peter Peregrinus make his studies in magnetism; not until the sixteenth century

171

did William Gilbert add a little to the knowledge of magnetism, and begin to study electricity.

After that, little by little, new knowledge was revealed; slowly its bright design took shape. Among the men and women who studied electricity and the subjects that were associated with it, were rich and poor, old and young, famed and obscure. They carried on their work in Germany and France, Italy and Russia, England and America, and many other places. Each one added only a little to the knowledge that had gone before. Slowly, through patience and hard work, they uncovered many of the secrets of science.

They studied electricity and magnetism, and found them to be related; they found out how to generate electricity and send it out along wires and through the air. They studied the atoms of which the earth is composed, and learned how to free the tiny electric particles of which they are made. They studied light, and found that the earth's atmosphere is filled with many radiations that the human eye cannot see.

172

Now, because of the work they did, the life of men around them changed. Not much more than a century ago the streets and houses had been dimly lighted with flickering lamps; now they blazed with electricity. Then, the news was carried by word of mouth, or letters were sent by slow packets or stage coaches; now, it was flashed around the world by radio waves that traveled with the speed of light. Now, electricity flashed along copper wires to turn the factory wheels; electric furnaces glared in the big steel plants; and electronic devices opened doors, counted, sorted, and matched colors.

Now, the electron microscope revealed hitherto unknown viruses, and X-ray treated diseases that had before been baffling. Now, pilots of the great airships steered their craft safe to the airports, riding the beam; and there was radar transmission to the moon. Now, a great atomic bomb was made with power to destroy a whole city, and men talked of using the power of such a bomb in the new atomic age.

While the world was changing round them, the scientists worked on. They used the new devices their researches had made possible, for these men, too, were part of the new age. But to create such devices had not been their object. Something in them had made them want to understand the old mysteries that had baffled men so long. They wanted, more than anything else, to explore what Sir Isaac Newton once called "the great ocean of truth."

Some of them had sought to understand the behavior of the magnet and to control electricity; some had sought to understand the material substance of the earth and had released atomic energy; some had sought to understand the nature of light, and had discovered the radiations that quiver through the universe. In the end they found that all three fields were one. For in all three they saw manifestations of the cosmic fire itself.

As they worked—in barren rooms, in universities, in great industrial laboratories—their researches extended farther and farther, until at length they were sending expeditions to study radiation around the world and up into the stratosphere. And all the inventions and devices at which the men of the new age marveled seemed unimportant to them. For they had traced the cosmic fire until their research had taken them beyond the earth, into the wide empty spaces that lie between the stars.

RECENT inventions have changed life so much that a man of today would feel very strange if he had to live as his great-grandfather, his grandfather, or even his father lived.

A hundred years ago, for instance, bicycles had no pedals. The bicycle of seventy years ago had a large front wheel, with pedals fixed to its hub, and a small back wheel. It was some years before modern bicycles, invented more than sixty years ago, became common.

Seventy years ago, telephones were fitted with a handle for ringing the exchange. Later came phones which rang automatically when the receiver was lifted from the hook. Dial telephones came into use less than twenty years ago.

In flying, the last century has brought even greater changes. Soon after the Declaration of Independence, two French brothers named Montgolfier made a large globe-shaped linen bag with a hole in the bottom. They lit a fire

A Hundred Years of Inventions

BY LANCELOT HOGBEN

Illustrated by Mauro Caputo

under the hole, and as the air inside the bag became hot their balloon rose, because the hot air inside was lighter than the air outside.

Within a few months other balloons were made and filled with hydrogen, a lighter-than-air gas, and people were soon making the first balloon ascents. But for many years balloonists could go only where the wind blew them, and it was not until the year 1900 that Count von Zeppelin made the first really

175

successful gasoline-driven and hydrogen-filled airship. Airships were often used to carry passengers until about 1930, when they were gradually replaced by planes. Balloons are seldom used today except for observing weather conditions at high altitudes.

Modern flying began in 1903 when Wilbur and Orville Wright of Dayton, Ohio, fitted a glider with propeller and engine. In 1905 they flew twenty-five miles in half an hour. Thirty-five years later, fighter planes roared into battle at four hundred miles an hour; now jet planes can travel faster than sound.

EVEN thousands of years ago it was known that numbers had many wonderful things in their make-up. Some numbers could be divided by 2, with nothing left over, but others could not.

For example, not using fractions:

6 can be divided by 2; that is, 6 divided by 2 equals 3.

Neither 7 nor 11 can be divided by 2.

Numbers that can be divided by 2 were called even numbers, and numbers that cannot be so divided were called odd numbers.

The numbers 2, 4, 10, 18, 36, 78, 102, are even.

The numbers 3, 9, 11, 25, 47, 69, 401, are odd, and so are 1007 and 2,000,001.

In the old days people called the odd numbers lucky, and the even ones unlucky. Even today there are people who are superstitious and silly enough to do the same.

Three or four thousand years ago it was discovered that some odd numbers can be divided by other numbers. For example 9 can be divided by 3, and 15 can be divided by 3, and 25 can be divided by 5. Others, such as 3, 11, and 47, cannot be divided at all. These are called prime numbers.

The people of thousands of years ago thought that prime numbers were mysterious and divine. Most people then could not count above their ten fingers. The prime numbers below

These Curious Numbers of Ours

BY DAVID EUGENE SMITH

Illustrated by Marjorie Saynor and Kenneth Symonds

ten are 3, 5, and 7. These were therefore thought to be the most mysterious of all, and of these the 3 and 7 stood highest because neither was so familiar as 5, which equals the number of fingers on a hand.

This is why we have "three cheers" and "seven days in the week," and so on with many uses of 3 and 7. People vote when they are 3 x 7 years old and they are thought to "come down" in 7 days with some kinds of illnesses.

178

Although Athens was the center of learning in the world about twenty-three hundred years ago, even the wisest Athenians thought that 3 and 7 were the most mysterious of all numbers.

The educated Greeks spoke of the Seven Wonders of the World. These were:

The pyramids of Egypt.
The lighthouse built by Ptolemy Philadelphus in the Bay
    of Alexandria at the mouth of the river Nile in Egypt.
The temple of Artemis (Diana) at Ephesus in Asia Minor.
The statue of Zeus (Jupiter) by the famous Greek sculptor
    Phidias, at Olympia.
The Mausoleum at Halicarnassus.
The Colossus at Rhodes, a gigantic statue of Apollo.
The walls and hanging gardens of Babylon.

Except for the pyramids, not one of these would seem very wonderful to us today. Even in their day they were no more wonderful than many other things, but the people thought that there was something wonderful about the number seven. There were also Seven Liberal Arts, the first five being arithmetic, music, geometry, astronomy, and grammar. Astronomers spoke of Seven Heavens and thought there were only seven planets.

Today we still speak of the seven seas when we mean the oceans, although no geographer names more oceans than the Atlantic, Pacific, Indian, Arctic, and Antarctic.

KING Hammurabi had just returned to his palace when he heard the new moon signal. He heard it clearly, for the king's residence in Babylon was just across the square from the big temple, the one with the tallest tower in the city. It was from this tower that the high priest, who was also the official calendar maker, would watch the heavens as the sun was setting, and at the first sight of the new moon he would blow his horn.

In the kingdom of Babylonia, a new month was begun when a new moon was seen, and one of the high priest's duties was to keep a regular lookout for the crescent moon. Soon after giving this new-moon signal, he walked down from the tower and crossed over to the palace where he reported to the king.

"This is going to be a thirteen-month year," he said. "The people should be so informed."

Hammurabi had made many improvements in the laws, and in the other affairs of his country. But he never had tried to regulate the calendar. He would not have dared to do this because, like other Babylonians, he believed the moon was a god. If the moon-god caused a mixup of the calendar, it just had to be accepted.

Counting Moons

BY RUTH BRINDZE

*Illustrated by
Helene Carter*

"The sooner the people get the news, the better it will be," he thought, so he called for the royal scribe and dictated the following message:

"This month is Elulu. The coming month shall therefore be called 2nd Elulu."

180

The king pressed his royal seal into the soft clay on which the message had been written (kings did not sign their names to letters or to anything else in those days), and messengers were dispatched to the governors of the important cities of Babylonia. Some of these messengers rode off on donkeys, but many messengers traveled by boat, for there were numerous rivers and canals in the kingdom, and water travel was easy and fast.

News that there was to be an extra month spread quickly, and, even though Babylonians were accustomed to such changes, many merchants grumbled and complained. Those who expected to collect bills at the end of the year grumbled the most, for now they would have to wait an extra month to collect their money.

The reason for Babylonia's calendar trouble was that, although the months were figured according to the moon, the year was measured according to the sun.

Actually, there are a little more than 29 days between new moons (this is how long it takes the moon to travel around our planet, the earth, and to be visible again as a thin crescent). But the sun year is a little more than 365 days. The two systems of moon months and sun year could not be made to fit together evenly, so every once in a while an extra month had to be added to round out a year.

The high priest was a first-rate scientist, and he knew how to measure a sun year. He could do this without any special instruments. All he needed was a single stake, or marker, driven firmly into the ground. He used this marker to measure the sun's position at the moment it appeared on the horizon at dawn.

The high priest had been taught by older priests how to do this. The method had been known for a long time. At sunrise he would stand directly behind the marker, facing the sun, and

181

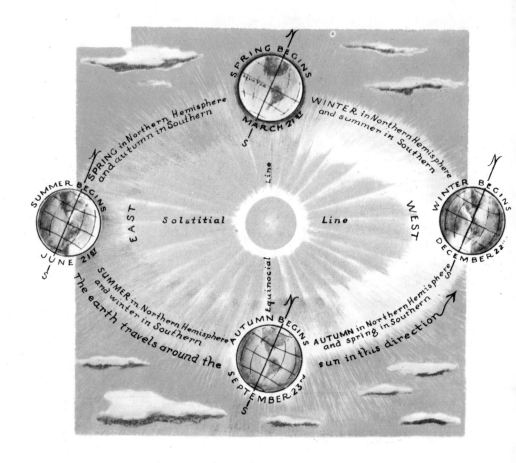

on most mornings he would see the sun rise a little to one side or the other of the marker. But there were special mornings when the sun appeared on a direct line with the marker, or exactly in the east. These were the days for which the high priest watched, for such days were celebrated as holidays in Babylonia.

We call these days the *equinoxes,* and there is one about March 21 and another about September 23. On these days the hours of daylight and of darkness are equal.

The Babylonian scientists kept careful records of the num-

182

ber of times they saw the sun rise directly in back of the marker. Each time, according to their calendar system, marked the end of half a year.

Of course, they did not know the scientific reason for the equinoxes. They could not possibly have known the reason, because the Babylonians believed that the sun and the stars revolved around the earth. We know that the equinoxes occur because the earth travels around the sun and because the earth's axis is tilted. As our planet, the earth, makes its round-the-sun journey, the north pole is sometimes closer to the sun than the south pole. But twice during this annual journey the north pole and the south pole are exactly the same distance from the sun. This happens on the days that we call the equinoxes.

In Babylonia, one of these days was celebrated as the New Year's holiday, the most exciting of the year. There was a great parade in which Hammurabi and other state officials took part, and as boys and girls and grown-ups watched from the side lines, vendors of sweets made of honey and nuts passed through the crowds, just as peddlers do nowadays with popcorn, candies and soda.

Why didn't the Babylonians keep their calendar by the sun alone? There are many possible explanations: First, the moon is a convenient timekeeper, since it appears, grows, and disappears at such regular and short intervals; secondly, the Babylonians thought that the moon-god was more important than the sun-god and wished to give it first place. They thought that the moon was the father of the sun and of all the stars. Yet the Babylonians did make many discoveries about the stars; in fact, some of our experts believe it is because of the Babylonians' star discoveries that we count seven days to a week.

Among all the twinkly stars, they saw five that shine with

a steady light (we call them planets), and since these were considered rare, they were watched closely. From these observations the stargazers discovered that the planets, like the sun and the moon, seem to move across the heavens.

We know that planets are pieces which have been thrown off by the sun and that they have no light of their own. They shine because they reflect the sun's light. And although the moon is not a planet, it also reflects the light of the sun, and so does our planet, the earth. If we were able to fly thousands of miles into the sky, we might see the earth shining.

The ancient Babylonians thought the five planets they recognized were gods, and one day was set aside for the worship of each. The people of Babylonia already worshiped the

Wedge-shaped cuneiform writing which was used at the time Hammurabi was king of Babylonia.

HAMMURABI

sun on one day and the moon on another. Now there were five other gods to honor, and so the Babylonians began to count the days in groups of seven, just as we count seven days to a week.

But how was this custom of old Babylonia carried forward to our world? We do not construct buildings as the Babylonians did, nor do we dress in Babylonian fashion. Why, then, do we count days by seven?

Many different explanations are given by people who can read the wedge-shaped (cuneiform) writing of the Babylonians and the records left by other Eastern nations, but the correct answer seems to be that our calendar is divided into weeks of seven days because the ancient Jews happened to know about the Babylonian system.

In any event, when the Jews wrote their story of the beginning of the world, in the book called the Bible, they divided time into seven-day periods. Because the Bible became the most important book in the world, most nations adopted the custom of dividing time into weeks consisting of seven days.

Perhaps if the skygazers of Babylonia had had sharper eyes, or if they had had telescopes and other instruments such as our astronomers use, we might have had a week of 10 days, for eight planets can be seen from our own planet, the earth. Just think what a change it might have made in our entire schedule if people who lived thousands of years ago had counted eight planets in the sky, and had dedicated one day to each, in addition to the moon's day and the sun's day! Schools might have been in session for eight days in a row, and grown-ups who work in factories and offices might also have had fewer holidays. If eight planets had been seen, our calendar and our entire schedule for work and play might have been different.

THERE is an old story that one of the gods was born lame. Because his mother did not like to see him limping, she sent him away. He came down to earth and lived on an island in the sea. His name was Vulcan. In pity for his lameness another god gave him the knowledge of how to work with gold and silver, bronze and iron. That gift was of great use to the gods and to men, for the lame smith used it well.

He made all the swords and shields of the great heroes of olden time. He made the great bronze palaces in which the gods and goddesses lived. The great thunderbolts that were hurled at the earth when Jupiter, the king of all the gods, was angry, were made by Vulcan. Down in his shop under Mount Etna he made everything out of metals that the world needed. People said that the smoke that came from the top of the volcano, called Mount Vesuvius, was from Vulcan's forge. The word "volcano" comes from Vulcan's name.

The First Metal Workers

BY GRACE KINER

Illustrated by
Ezra Jack Keats

For a long time men were satisfied with the tools they knew how to make from stone and bone. They were busy on their little farms and with their flocks of sheep and goats. Some of them, when they were hunting for flint, had found pieces of a red rock that could be pounded with a stone hammer into any shape that was wanted. This red material was copper. It is a soft metal and can be very easily changed in shape by hammering.

186

The men who found copper used it to make axe points and hoes, but they found that it was so soft that it was not as good to work with as the stone. It would not stay sharp. There was very little of it too, because copper is almost always mixed with rock and is not in lumps by itself but must be melted out.

Then some man used rocks that had copper in them to put around his fire and found that when the rocks were hot the copper melted and ran out. He saw that this metal was the same as the red lumps he had found. Then he went to look for rocks that had the streaks of red in them, put them in the fire, and got out the copper by melting.

It didn't take him long after that to see that if he made a hole the shape of an axe in the sand and let the melted copper run into it and get hard he would have an axe that was very much prettier than his old stone one. This was an easier way to make axes than pounding and chipping stone, too.

There isn't very much copper in the world, so that the early men had to go long distances in search of it. When they were looking for it they found another metal even prettier than copper. It was white and shining when they melted it, but it was so soft that it was no good for spear points or hammers. This was tin. Once when one of the men was making an axe or hammer head of copper he didn't have quite enough to fill his mold so he filled it with melted tin. He must have been very much surprised when he used the axe, to find that it was harder and better than most of the copper tools were. He had made

a great discovery—how to make bronze out of copper and tin.

Bronze is a metal made by mixing copper and tin. These are both very soft metals, but when they are melted and stirred together they make a metal that is almost as hard as iron. The men who had been using stone tools didn't throw away their stone things, but they did begin to use the bronze knives and axes when they could get them.

By grinding the edge with a soft stone, a bronze knife can be made much sharper than any man could possibly chip a flint knife. Bronze can be melted and pounded into all kinds of shapes, which can't be done with stone.

When the men were looking for copper and tin they found other metals: silver, gold and lead. The lead was used to make images for the gods, because it was too soft to be of any use for tools. Silver and gold were very scarce and they were used just as men do today—to make jewelry to wear. Sometimes they made gold spears and other weapons to put into the graves with kings, so that they would have fine weapons to carry in the happy hunting grounds to which they were going. They thought the next world was much like this one.

They found iron at the same time they were looking for

copper, but they did not use it as soon because it was hard to melt out of the rock, because it was not as pretty as the copper and tin, and because it rusted away.

By the time that most people were using bronze to make weapons, tools and ornaments, they were also weaving woolen and linen cloth to use for clothing. The poor people still used skins to dress in, but the rich wore fine garments and many pieces of jewelry.

In the northern countries the men wore woolen tunics, a kind of shirt that reached to the knees and was fastened with a belt around the waist. As soon as men found out how to use metals they made safety pins, very much like the ones we have today, to fasten their tunics at the neck. These pins were made of gold and silver and bronze and were used as jewelry in those days.

Over the tunic a thick long coat without sleeves, much like our capes, was thrown in cold weather. This was fastened on the shoulder with an ornamental pin. Tall pointed caps were worn on their heads, and shoes made out of leather were kept on their feet with long laces of leather that were wound around their legs.

In the warmer countries people wore linen clothes. Where it was very warm people did not wear any clothes at all for a very long time. They painted their bodies, or tattooed them as some of the wild tribes in Africa do even to this very day.

The women wore much more fancy clothing than the men. They had short jackets with short sleeves and long full skirts with ruffles on them, held up with a wide belt. The belts were often colored in two or three colors and had tassels or beautiful buckles made of gold or bronze sometimes set with jewels.

Rich women wore a great deal of jewelry. They had necklaces, buckles for their belts and for their shoulders, brooches to fasten the necks of their dresses, and hairpins made of gold. They put up their hair in nets and had fine combs of bronze or ivory.

The men liked fine gold pins and buckles, too. They did not cut their hair and they, too, had fine bronze combs. Some had beards; but we know that some of them shaved because we have found many good razors of bronze buried with them.

ORANGES sometimes grow on lemon trees, but it does not happen naturally. An orange grower often puts oranges on his lemon trees by grafting or budding. A man might buy some land to use for an orange grove and then find that the soil was not good for orange trees, but excellent for lemons. He does not become discouraged and sell his farm but instead lets some lemon trees get a good start. When he is sure the trees are strong and healthy, he goes to someone who has orange trees and gets some buds. He is careful to cut buds only from the very best trees. We usually think of buds as growing into flowers or leaves, but branches come from them also. This man will cut a bud from the orange tree in such a way that there will be a small oval-shaped piece of bark clinging to it. Then he quickly cuts a T-shaped slit in the back of the lemon tree and slips the orange bud underneath. He covers the cuts with wax to keep the moisture from drying out and sometimes winds raffia or twine about the stem to hold the bud in place.

Man-Made Plants

BY JANET McGILL

Illustrated by D. Alexandroff

If he has done a good job, the bud will begin to grow into a branch. That branch will bear oranges, not lemons. After the branch has had a good start and has produced enough leaves to make food for the tree, he may cut off all the lemon branches. Then he has an orange tree, but the roots are still those of the lemon tree. He can do this to his whole grove. It is not hard to do. The workman must be careful of just one thing. The growing part of a tree is just under the bark. He must make his

191

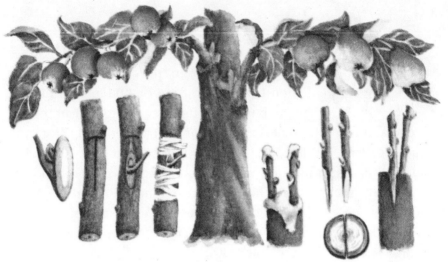

cuts so that the growing part of the orange tree and the growing part of the lemon tree fit into each other exactly. If he cuts too deep or not deep enough, the bud will not be able to grow.

Budding has made it possible to grow oranges in many places where they did not grow before. One kind of orange can be budded onto the roots of another kind. For example, Florida oranges are very sweet and juicy, but they will not grow except in very warm climates. A certain kind of Japanese orange will stand much colder weather, but its fruit is sour and bitter. Someone thought of putting the Florida buds onto the Japanese trees, and now it is possible to raise Florida oranges much farther north than formerly. You can see that there is a great advantage in being able to do this.

Often people who do not raise fruit to sell have fun making experiments with budding. A family may have room for just one tree in its yard. They probably will plant a lemon tree, for it is very hardy. Later they can bud onto that tree, oranges, grapefruit, and tangerines. Maybe they will have several different kinds of oranges. It is not at all unusual in California to see four kinds of fruit growing on one single tree.

The different kinds of fruit must be closely related, as oranges and lemons are. You cannot put apples on lemon trees, but you can grow apples on pear trees. There is a grove of prune trees in California now whose roots are the roots of almond trees. It is fairly easy to tell which trees will exchange this way by looking at the seeds. Orange and lemon seeds are alike, so are apple and pear, and prune pits are like almond pits.

It is a curious fact that apple trees grown from seeds never have as good fruit as the apple which produced the seed. The seeds from a big juicy apple might be planted and develop into trees which bear small sour fruit. Because this is true, farmers do not raise apple trees from seed but buy little trees from the nursery man. However, if a farmer wanted to take the time and trouble, he could get good trees by grafting, which is what the nursery man does. Grafting is very like budding, but is a little harder to do. It means attaching the twigs of one tree to a branch of another.

This is what often happens: A farmer has one fine apple tree. The apples are big, juicy, mellow, and of a lovely red color. Around his orchard are several little seedlings from these same apples. They are strong and healthy, but he knows the apples they bear will not be as good as those of the parent tree. He cuts off one of these seedlings just above the ground and makes a notch. Then, from his good tree, he cuts two twigs that have several buds, and he shapes their ends like a wedge. He fits these into the notch, one on each side, taking great care that the growing parts of the stem and the twigs come together. Then he ties the twigs in place with raffia and covers the cuts with wax to keep out rain and bugs. If he has done his work carefully, the twigs will grow just as well as on their own tree, and in a few years he will have delicious fruit.

193

The seedling to which the twigs are grafted is called the *stock*, and the twigs which are grafted on are called *scions*. There are several ways of grafting—that is of cutting and fitting —but the principle is always the same. The growing part of the stock and the scion must fit together. The growing part of the tree is just under the bark.

Sometimes grafting is used for another purpose. In France, the largest industry is making wine from grapes. Some years ago all the grape vines began to die. It was found that some plant disease had attacked the roots. For a time it seemed that all the vineyards would be lost. It was a very serious situation but at last somebody discovered that American grape vines did not catch this disease. They were immune to it. No matter how close they were placed to the diseased plants they grew and thrived. The French began to plant American grapes. However, the grapes from the transplanted vines were not sweet enough to make good wine. Therefore they grafted their French vines to the American roots. Now the grapes were just as they were before the disease attacked them. You could not tell the difference in the fruit, but the roots were strong and healthy. Grafting saved the French vineyards.

The big, brilliantly white shasta daisy is not a natural but one that was created from three less attractive daisies. Luther Burbank, a world-famous experimenter with plants, improved and changed many plants in a way that seems almost like magic by using a method called "crossing." He had always been fond of daisies, but the American field daisy is not a very beautiful flower. It is strong and hardy and has a great many blossoms, but they are small and straggly. The stems are crooked and not very tall. In England there was a daisy much larger than ours with coarser stems and flowers. In Japan, there was a small daisy whose petals were so white they were almost dazzling. Mr. Burbank thought how wonderful it would be to have a daisy large and tall like the English one, strong and full of blossoms like the American, and a brilliant white like the Japanese. The shasta daisy has all these good qualities and this is how Mr. Burbank did it:

He got the very best seed he could find from the three different kinds of daisies and planted them. When they bloomed, he cross-pollinated them. That means that instead of letting the pollen from one kind of daisy, say the American, fall upon the pistils of the same kind, he took the pollen and with a small brush sprinkled it carefully on another kind, either the English or the Japanese. He saw to it that each flower received pollen from a different kind of daisy. He did

not know which combination would be the best, so he tried a great many different ones. After the daisies had all been pollinated, he tied little bags over them to protect them from any wandering bee with pollen on his legs that might come along and spoil the experiment. When the seeds formed from these flowers, he saved and planted them. Later, when the flowers came from these seeds, he studied them carefully. Just as a little girl may have curly hair like her mother and blue eyes like her father, so some of these flowers were large and tall like the English daisy and a beautiful white like the Japanese. Whenever a flower had a good quality that he wanted to keep, he crossed the pollen from it with another good flower and saved the seed. When the plants grew from this seed, he saved only the best ones. Those that were tall, straight, white, large, strong, and many-blossomed were chosen and he burned the rest. He selected the seed and planted it every year for eight years, destroying always those flowers that were not just right. All of this time was necessary because plants inherit bad traits from their ancestors just as people do. He wanted to be sure that none of the seeds would produce flowers that were small, straggly, or a dirty white color.

At the end of eight years he was sure that the seeds would produce only beautiful flowers. Then he gave the seed to others, and soon there were shasta daisies growing in gardens all over the country. He named the flower for Mt. Shasta, a beautiful mountain peak in California, which is covered with shining white snow all through the year.

Botanists call a flower like the shasta daisy a hybrid because it is produced by crossing the pollen of different kinds of plants, and it inherits the best points of each. Most hybrids are formed only by two kinds of plants. The shasta daisy is unusual because it comes from three.

196

ENGINEERING has come to be an important element in our civilization.

Traffic, commerce, and transportation around the world will increase; so it stands to reason that the civil engineer will always find work to do.

What are some of the problems the bridgebuilder of the future will be called upon to solve? We can discuss only a few. One of them is a problem that the engineer faced fully for the first time some years ago. On July 1, 1940, the Tacoma Narrows Bridge at Puget Sound, Washington, was opened. It was the third longest bridge in the world—a suspension bridge with a main span of 2,800 feet. From the day of its opening the peculiar heaving movement of the bridge attracted attention. Motorists came from miles around to drive over "Galloping Gertie," as the bridge was nicknamed, to enjoy the thrill of driving over a galloping roller coaster.

Bridges Help Us Every Day

BY DAVID B. STEINMAN

Illustrated by George Bobritzky

For four months the bridge stood. Then on November 7, 1940, it fell, crashing into the waters of Puget Sound. Fortunately no human lives were lost; the only casualty was a dog. On the morning of that day there was a wind of thirty-five to forty-two miles an hour whipping up the waves, and the bridge began to heave up and down as much as three feet. Alarmed when the movement kept up for three hours, the highway authorities stopped all traffic over the bridge.

Soon it developed a twisting motion, and the opposite sides of the bridge were rising and falling as much as twenty-eight

197

feet. At one moment, one edge of the roadway was twenty-eight feet higher than the other; the next moment it was twenty-eight feet lower. The roadway was tilted forty-five degrees from the horizontal one way, and then forty-five degrees the other way. The bridge looked as if it were made of rubber, not of steel and concrete.

Finally, at 11 A.M., the main span tore away from the suspenders. The supporting girders ripped away from the floor like a zipper.

The cause of the catastrophe was soon recognized by bridgebuilders. It was a combination of two factors more marked in this bridge than in any other. One was the extreme flexibility of the span; the other was a peculiar characteristic of the bridge best described as "aerodynamic instability."

Let me describe the flexibility—the first factor—now. The Tacoma Narrows Bridge was the most slender yet built. What proved critical was the *vertical* slenderness of the span. It had been generally agreed that the supporting truss or girder should be not less than one-hundredth the length of span. But the stiffening girders of the Tacoma Bridge were only eight feet deep in a span of 2,800 feet—or a ratio of one in three-hundred-and-fifty.

The other factor—the newly discovered "aerodynamic instability"—was the result of the use of solid plate girders with a solid floor. The consequence was that the wind could not go *through* the bridge. As a result, the motion of the wind, combined with the motion of the bridge, gave it a repeated "kick

upwards" that caused it to undulate with increasing intensity.

You have all heard that an army marching across a suspension bridge is ordered to break step. Any constant and rhythmic impact will set the bridge in motion, and if there is no restraining device to stop or to interrupt these waves, they may build up.

The Tacoma Narrows Bridge was perfectly safe for all the loads and forces that it had been designed to bear. But in common with many other bridges up to that time, it had not been designed for the "aerodynamic" effect of wind load. The engineering profession had not been awakened to this effect and had no data upon which to draw conclusions. Fortunately, the aerodynamic problem has been solved so that suspension bridges can now be designed with assured safety.

This is an example of the problems a modern engineer must face. The engineer has to develop new design forms, new erection methods, and new materials. This brings up another problem. Right now the bridgebuilder is using a brand new structural material—aluminum. And he has to use a whole new set of specifications when building with this material which is stronger than steel but much lighter, weighing only one-third as much as steel. As you can realize, the old formulas for steel cannot apply here. New alloy steels are also being invented, and we are constantly adding to our knowledge about the behavior of these new bridge materials.

Looking at another kind of problem, we approach the application of mathematics. Certain kinds of bridges, like hingeless arches and continuous spans, have only now come into general use because the methods of computation have been improved and simplified. These mathematical advances have led to the development of new types of bridges.

There are five fundamental types: the beam or girder

199

Tacoma Narrows Bridge in twisting motion

Brooklyn Bridge, between New York City and Brooklyn, is a suspension bridge.

bridge, the arch, the truss, the cantilever, the suspension. Now a new popular type for small bridges is the "rigid-frame" bridge. It looks like a beam bridge, but it does not act or work like one. A beam bridge consists of three separate members—two uprights or verticals (the piers), with a horizontal beam laid across the two uprights. A rigid-frame looks just like a beam bridge, but instead of being in three pieces, it is cast or built in one piece, a structure shaped like an inverted U. Perhaps you, as one of the engineers of the future, will invent other *new* types.

Another field of knowledge recently explored by engineers is called "soil mechanics"—a scientific study of how various kinds of soils act as foundation materials. We still do not know all there is to know about this subject.

But the biggest challenge to the engineer in the future will have to do more and more with problems outside of the highly specialized and technical fields. They will, for example, deal with city-planning and with long-range designs for highways. We need more superhighways, turnpikes, and parkways. The engineer must be responsible for planning these networks and building them so that they will be safe, efficient, economical and beautiful.

The bridges of the future will be gateways to knowledge—

200

Landwasser Viaduct in Switzerland is an arch bridge for railroads.

knowledge of all sorts: mathematics, economics, geology, metallurgy, physics. These bridges will increase in size, strength, and beauty.

Have you ever imagined what the world would be like without bridges? Suppose you are walking to the football field with all your equipment—helmet, football and so on. Then suddenly the sidewalk ends. In front of you is a deep ravine, and you must cross it to get to the field. Perhaps you could scramble down one side of the ravine and up the other. But what would you do with your gear?

Or suppose you are riding in an automobile along a fine highway, when suddenly it comes to a stop on the bank of a broad river. Maybe you could swim across, but the automobile couldn't. Our great transcontinental railroads could not have been built without the bridges to carry the trains over rivers, ravines, and canyons.

Once we realize how important bridges really are as a part of our great transportation system, we begin to look at them—actually to see them for the first time. To appreciate a bridge

one needs not only to walk over it but to stand off at a distance and look at it broadside; then to go down under it and study its construction. The best way to see bridges is to take a boat ride on the river, or to walk through the valley.

Primitive people or pioneers living in a new country, as our ancestors did a couple of hundred years ago, are greatly limited in their movement, for the only lanes of travel are footpaths, pack trails, and local wagon roads. As Europe and America developed, stagecoaches were built. For these, paved roads were necessary. Next came canals, and shortly after them railroads—and finally automobiles. All these means of transportation required bridges—and developed the bridgebuilder's art. The American spirit, both daring and practical, is especially well adapted to excel in this development.

The greatest change in bridgebuilding came with the steam engine. It cannot jump over valleys or rivers; it must have bridges and exceedingly heavy ones. The new material—iron and steel—became important in bridgebuilding at that time because it could bear such heavy loads and yet was easier to erect and cheaper than stone. There are over 90,000 steel bridges on 240,000 miles of railroad in the United States.

Since about 1920 the tremendous increase in highway traffic has created a whole new phase of bridge construction. Bridges of hitherto unheard-of length and size have been needed and therefore built, as well as tens of thousands of small bridges. The number of highway bridges of steel and concrete exceeds 250,000 on our three million miles of roads and highways. The total investment in these bridges is over three billion dollars.

A good example of what a bridge can do to improve transportation is the new Chesapeake Bay Bridge. Instead of lining up and waiting for the ferry to take a few cars across this arm

Chesapeake Bay Bridge is a highway bridge.

of the sea, we can now drive quickly over it in less than ten minutes. The bridge—really a string of bridges—stretches for more than four miles over the bay and connects superhighways from New England to Florida. For the first time now, we can travel the length of the eastern coast over a continuous highway, without any breaks. And this means, too, that we by-pass the congested areas of Baltimore and Washington. This structure is one of the country's big engineering feats.

When you stop to think of it, you realize that all large cities are on bodies of water, generally a river, and the city lies on both sides. This is natural, because people assembled where there was good water transportation (in the days before railroads). Commerce or trade is necessary for the growth of a nation. Rome is on the Tiber, Paris on the Seine, London on the Thames, New York on the Hudson, on the East River, on the ocean. Obviously, bridges are most necessary in these cities, to fulfill the needs of transportation and business.

The city of New York furnishes an excellent example. Over 750,000 automobiles and trucks cross its fifteen highway

203

bridges to Manhattan Island in a single day—besides more than 700,000 passengers who cross daily in rapid transit trains or buses.

Bridges are a measure of how far civilization has advanced. With the growing needs of intercommunication, of travel, and of trade—in fact, as we grow into one world—we build more and greater bridges. Engineers in the past century have advanced the science and art of bridgebuilding more rapidly than the builders in all the preceding centuries. And the generation just past more than broke the record of the preceding generation in building bigger and bolder spans. So it will go on; your generation should break all previous records in the realm of engineering.

And the engineer realizes that he is building more than a bridge; he is fostering understanding and good will between peoples. These structures must be strong and enduring and beautiful. In the words of John Ruskin, nineteenth-century English author, the engineer has a creed:

"Therefore when we build, let us think that we build forever."

Henry Hudson Bridge in New York City is a deck-arch bridge.

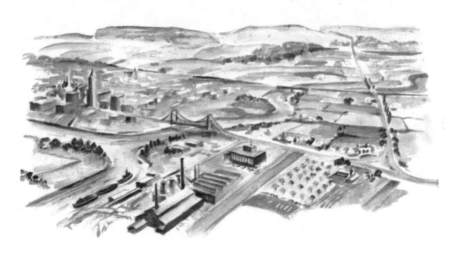

Bridges

BY JAMES S. TIPPETT

Illustrated by Clare Bice

I LIKE a bridge—
Any kind of bridge at all.
A great steel bridge
With towers stiff and tall;
An old covered bridge
That spans a waterfall;
A hewn-stone bridge
With its rugged floor and wall;
A railroad bridge
Where freight trains slowly crawl;
A wooden bridge,
A cement bridge,
Whether big or small;
Yes, I like a bridge—
Just any kind of bridge at all.

Clipper Ship

BY NANCY BYRD TURNER

THEY built her out of sturdy oak
Hewn from the woods behind the town;
Her clean mast was a splendid pine,
The children of the port came down

To see her growing, day by day,
To watch her rising, part by part.
She seemed to them like their own land,
So sound, so straight, so true of heart.

The timbers rolled, the hammers rang,
The workmen told old salty tales. . . .
And then at last she seaward stood,
With all the world's winds in her sails!

Forward she took her steadfast way,
The ship their dreams had helped to build;
Her keen prow cut the pushing tide,
Her bright wake foamed, her white sails filled.

She seemed to them America,
Their great ship, set for any gale.
They lifted up a song for her—
She would not fail! She would not fail!

206

PEOPLE have wondered about asbestos for more than two thousand years.

In olden times no poor man could own any of the "magic flax" which would not catch fire even in the hottest blaze. Only a few men had ever seen it.

Men spoke with awe when they told each other about "magic flax" or "magic cotton-stone," as they called asbestos. Many of the stories they told were true.

One upon a time, as long ago as four hundred years before Christ was born, a sculptor named Callimachus worked for weeks and weeks to make a lamp of solid gold. It was for the statue of the Greek goddess Athene. This shining, graceful, golden lamp was one of the most beautiful lamps in all the world. Men walked miles and miles to see it and to admire it. Yet, strangely enough, they talked as much about the wick that was in the lamp as they did about the golden lamp itself. The wick was more valuable than gold, for it was made of "magic flax."

A Magic Mineral

BY
LILIAN HOLMES STRACK

Illustrated by Ernest Crichlow

So it was that all over Greece men talked and talked about the wick in the goddess Athene's lamp. In all the other lamps these men had ever seen, the wicks burned up along with the oil. Truly, the wick in Athene's lamp *was* made of something magic, they said. Why, the lamp could be kept burning, night and day, the whole year through with a flame which did not die.

Fire was precious in those primitive times. It took time

207

and hard work to light a fire even in warm dry weather. Wood was rubbed upon wood until a spark flared. The tiny blaze was shielded carefully, for even a breath of air might blow out the flame.

No wonder that everywhere in the world men cherished fire. Once upon a time in ancient Rome there was an ever-burning flame before the shrine of Vesta, goddess of the hearth and its fire. Many people worshipped gods and goddesses in those days. Vesta was one of the best-loved of all goddesses. She was the goddess of the home and of the fire for cooking food and for warmth from the fireplaces.

A sacred flame was always burning at the temple of the goddess of fire so that whenever men and women needed fire they could go to the temple for it. They could carry fire from the shrine to their homes.

It was a holy task, this keeping the fire burning before the shrine. This was something which could not be trusted to servants. The high priest chose six young girls to guard the flame so it would never die out. The six girls were the Vestal Virgins, and they were treated almost like princesses. They took turns in tending the flame and if one of them ever let it go out she was punished.

Many persons thought the lamp in the shrine of the goddess was sacred, that it was everlasting and would burn and last for endless time. An eternal or perpetual wick, it was called. The perpetual wick was made of the "magic flax" woven into a small tube through which the oil passed. The asbestos wick helped to keep the flame alight.

So it was that long before Christ was born "magic flax" was revered in two countries, in Greece and in the Roman Empire. Even then, in the Roman Empire, there was another use for asbestos. The "magic flax" or "magic cotton-stone"

208

was made into a rare and costly cloth to be used as "the funeral dress of kings." It was made into winding sheets or shrouds.

When the Roman kings died their bodies were burned or cremated and their ashes were put into beautiful urns to be cherished. Before the bodies were placed into the fires they were wrapped carefully in the magic cloth which would not burn. In this way the ashes of kings were kept apart from the fuel ashes. Only the revered ashes were saved.

No wonder that men thought of the "magic flax" as something almost sacred in those long ago days. It was hundreds of years later, an old story tells, that another king found another use for asbestos.

Once upon a time Charlemagne, King of the Franks, used an asbestos tablecloth to keep his Empire out of war. Charlemagne reigned from 768 to 814 A.D. It all happened at a time when Charlemagne and his warriors were not ready for battle. Charlemagne feared that Harun-al-Rashid and his horde of soldiers knew it. Something had to be done to keep the enemy from attacking them. Charlemagne thought of a plan which might work.

Charlemagne invited the envoys of his foes to a banquet. They came. On the long table was a white cloth woven of "magic cotton-stone" fibers. When everyone was seated, dinner was served. Servants brought in dish after dish, platter after platter of delicious food. At last, when nobody could eat another bite, the servants cleared away what was left of the food.

Charlemagne rose. His guests looked at him, thinking that he would talk about war. Charlemagne said nothing at all as he pulled the cloth from the table. Nearby, a fire was roaring in the fireplace. Charlemagne tossed the tablecloth into the flames.

The king turned back to his guests. There was music. Charlemagne clapped his hands, and dancers, actors and story-tellers came in.

When the fire burned low, Charlemagne rose and again he made sure that his guests were watching him. The king walked straight to the fireplace, stooped and lifted the tablecloth. It was whole and clean. Then, as calmly as if everyone cleaned a tablecloth by putting it into a fire and leaving it there for hours, Charlemagne put the cloth back upon the table.

The startled envoys tried to hide their surprise. Their eyes opened wide. They looked at each other quickly and then looked away. They didn't know what to think.

The envoys said their good-byes and hurried away. What they told their rulers, we don't know. Could it have been that Charlemagne had the power of magic? Magic was much feared in those days. With their own eyes they had seen Charlemagne put a tablecloth into a roaring crackling blaze. With their own eyes they had seen him take it out, hours later, whole and clean. If this wasn't magic, what was it? Thus the envoys made their report. There was no war. A ruler didn't start a war against a king who worked magic. Charlemagne was saved by his magic tablecloth.

So goes an old tale about Charlemagne and his rare table-cloth. Asbestos belonged to goddesses and kings then just as it did five hundred years later when Marco Polo saw it in a country thousands of miles from Charlemagne's Empire.

210

Marco Polo's longest trip was to the Empire of Tartary (now supposed to be Siberia). Slowly, Marco Polo crossed the burning deserts and climbed the high mountains which shut off this land from the rest of the world of that time. He reached cities never even heard of by the people of his native land. There in Tartary, Marco Polo heard men talk about a cloth which would not burn when men put it into a fire.

When Marco Polo asked about the cloth, the natives of Tartary told him a strange tale. The cloth, they said, was made of salamander skins. (A salamander looks much like a lizard. Superstitious people believed that salamanders were the spirits of fires and that salamanders could live and did live in the hottest of fires.) Yes, the Tartars said to Marco Polo, they had cut the skins from salamanders, slit them into strips and woven them into a fabric.

211

It was well known that the Great Khan, Ruler of the Empire of Tartary, had a cloth which would not burn. He wrapped precious things in it to protect them from fire. That cloth, the natives told Marco Polo, was made of salamander skins.

Never in all of his travels had Marco Polo seen a cloth made of the skins of salamanders. He had seen asbestos. He knew that in his home land of Italy, asbestos had been used for centuries in lamp wicks and in shrouds for kings. But in all the Roman Empire he had never seen a piece of cloth made of salamander skins.

The more Marco Polo heard of this magic cloth the more eager he became to see it. He had heard so many tales about the cloth that he supposed it really was made of salamander skins, whether it was fireproof or not. That is, he did until he saw it. Then he wondered. This "salamander" cloth looked much like the asbestos "funeral dress of kings" back in Italy. The more Marco Polo looked at the cloth the more he wondered. The more he wondered the more questions he asked. At last Marco Polo learned that the cloth was really made from "fibers not unlike wool which men dug from a mountain."

So go some of the old tales about this magic mineral. How much is true and how much is fiction in some of the stories we can only guess.

One thing we do know for certain about asbestos. We know that this strange fireproof mineral was millions of years in the making.

We know that once upon a time part of the earth was so hot that it was a liquid. When this liquid cooled it formed many rocks. These rocks are called *igneous* rocks.

We know that part of what is now land was covered by water. The waves beat against the rocks and broke them. Day after day, year after year, the great waves pounded the broken

212

rocks. They caught up bits and carried them away. These grains of sand and soil settled to the bottom of the water. They made *sedimentary* rock.

As the hot earth cooled, it shrank. As the outside or surface of the earth became smaller it pressed harder and harder on the rock in some places. The pressure squeezed and squeezed part of the rock until it was bent and twisted and crushed. All of this squeezing and twisting and crushing changed part of the igneous rock and part of the sedimentary rock—changed them so much that it made another or third kind of rock. This third kind of rock is called *metamorphic* rock. (Metamorphic means changed.)

All asbestos is changed rock, metamorphic rock. Nearly all of it comes from changed igneous rock. This changed igneous rock has been found in many places. It would take a lot of globe-whirling in order to point to all the countries where asbestos has been found. We would need to locate Australia, Canada, China, Cyprus, Finland, France, Germany, Hungary, India, Ireland, Japan, New Zealand, Rhodesia, Russia, Turkey, the Union of South Africa, the United States of America and Venezuela.

213

THE story of radium begins long ago, before anyone in the world ever heard of radium, with the silver mines in old Bohemia. Perhaps the story really should begin with the grumbling of the miners because the rich silver ore there was streaked by a greasy bluish-black ore called pitchblende. Everybody then thought that pitchblende was worthless. No doubt the miners complained and grumbled about the extra work it made as they stacked the pitchblende in great mountain-like dumps around the mines.

For years, even for centuries, those huge heaps of pitchblende stood there, neglected. Men thought them worse than worthless, for the stacks covered needed ground. Yet, thrown away and buried in the old piles all this time, was the then unknown element radium.

Since time began men have worked not only to find minerals but to find uses for minerals. So someone found out that in this old pitchblende there was a mineral called uranium. Uranium was useful. Men needed uranium to color glass, tile, and porcelain to shades of deep warm yellow, orange, and even a rich black.

The Rock That Glowed in the Dark

BY LILIAN HOLMES STRACK

Illustrated by Eleanor Mill

There was no grumbling about the great piles of pitchblende then. The eager miners hurried to the old dumps. Gladly they worked the huge piles over and over again for uranium. Then once again radium was thrown away.

So many of the things in the story of radium seem to have happened accidentally. This is one of them.

One evening a man who was working with pitchblende just happened to notice that it would glow in darkness for a while after it had been in sunlight. That was strange. None of the other ores the man had ever worked with glowed in the dark. The man tried it again, and then he showed it to some of his friends. There was no doubt about it, the ore did glow in the dark, and the darker it was the more the ore glowed. None of them could understand it. They had seen the light from fireflies, glowworms, and certain deep-sea fishes often, but not one of them had ever seen a glowing stone before. They were almost afraid of it. Men were superstitious in those days of long ago.

The more the men thought about it the stranger it seemed that a rock which had been under that pile since a time long before they were alive would flash a tiny light in the dark. There certainly was something queer about it. So the men talked and talked about the light from the pitchblende.

At last some of the scientists of that day heard about the glowing ore. They studied it but none of them learned the secret of it.

Then, much later, in 1896, something else "just happened" in Paris, France. Henri Becquerel, a scientist, happened to put some uranium on a photographic plate and leave it there for a while. The plate was covered with heavy black paper. He was startled, later, when he found that the uranium had taken its own picture! Where did the rays of light which took the picture come from? Nobody could take a picture without light of some kind. He wondered if the light which took the picture could be reflected rays. There was one way to make certain.

Henry Becquerel very carefully put his uranium into total darkness. He kept it there month after month. When the scientist was sure that there could be no reflected rays about the uranium, he slipped a photographic plate under the mineral

215

there in the midnight blackness. This time he was trying to take a picture.

The uranium didn't disappoint him. Henri Becquerel had his picture of uranium, a picture made in inky darkness, and without the use of a camera.

It was such a weird thing that the scientist told his friends about it. Among his hearers were two young scientists, Pierre and Marie Curie. Marie Curie was still a student. Perhaps it was the mystery which interested this young woman. What was there in that little piece of ore which could take its own picture? Nobody knew. Nobody seemed to know much, if anything, about the strange rays. Here was something outside the knowledge of men. The young Polish girl, wife of a French scientist, decided to find out about the rays.

Marie Curie didn't even know how to go about her task. It was something no one had ever done. So all she could do was to try first one way, then another.

Marie Curie was poor, so she had very little to work with.

216

She wore old clothes and she skimped on food so that she could buy more of the things she needed in her work. She worked and she worked. There seemed to be no way to find out the secret of the rays. All day long and until late into the night she studied and toiled. She tried this and she tried that. The days grew into weeks, the weeks into months and the months into years. Marie Curie continued to work and experiment, and still she couldn't learn what she wanted to know.

Sometimes, many times, Marie Curie forgot to eat. She was so eager to learn that often she forgot to sleep. But she never forgot to work. Month after month passed, and Marie Curie had nothing to show for her labor.

Then in 1898, she found a new element. She found something that no one else since time began had known. So that there could be no mistake about it, she started at the beginning and went over her work again and again until she was certain. She had found something new.

Marie Curie's husband, Pierre, started to work with her.

217

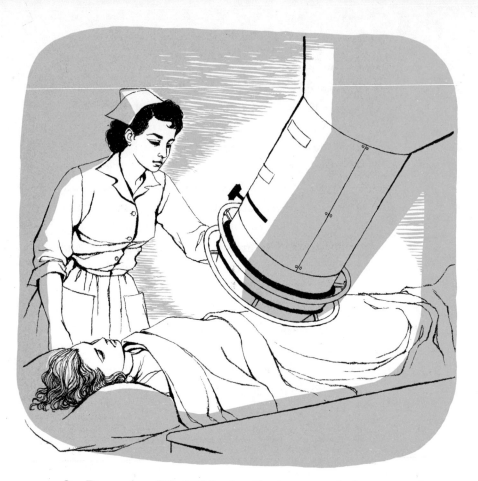

On December 26, 1898, the Curies named that new element RADIUM. On that day they—and they alone—knew that radium existed.

The scientists of that time, like the scientists of all times, demanded proof. "Show us some of this radium you have found," they said. "Let us see it. Give us some to weigh."

That was something the Curies could not do. They did not have enough radium to see or to weigh. What was worse, they did not have money to buy pitchblende so that they could prove they had found anything new. Pitchblende cost quite a lot of money now that uranium had been found in it. The best the Curies could do was to use worked-over pitchblende from

218

which the uranium had been taken. Perhaps, they hoped, perhaps there was some radium in it.

Pierre and Marie Curie took their worked-over ore to an old deserted shed. There, in the winter time, it was so cold that their fingers would get so stiff and clumsy it was hard for them to work. Inside the old shed, in the summer time, it was so hot and stuffy they could hardly breathe. For four winters and four summers they toiled there.

It was in 1902 that the Curies won. At last they had enough radium to weigh. They had a decigram of radium. A decigram is one-tenth of a gram. A whole gram will fill only the tip of a teaspoon. A penny weighs forty times as much as the radium for which the Curies had worked so many months.

This precious decigram, all the Curies had to show for more than four years of hard work, was given to science. Always when men think of radium they will think of the Curies, perhaps most of all of young Marie who set herself the task of finding out about the strange light in the ore.

Today, as when radium was first discovered by the Curies, trained physicians in hospitals use radium to fight the dreaded cancer, to burn away diseased tissues. Radium is used in treating or burning away birthmarks, warts, eczema, and other skin troubles. Simple radium burns heal quickly. However, at no time does the radium ever touch the patient. Through the little glass tube where it makes its home, radium sends out its magic rays.

Each year men are finding more ways to use radium to bring health and longer life to mankind. It brings hope and help to despairing people. It brings greater safety to men in industry, to men in the navy, and to other men on the sea in great ships. Surely it seems like magic when a bit of salts—only enough to fill part of the tip of a teaspoon—can do these things.

A MOLECULE is the very smallest particle of anything. A molecule of paper would be the smallest piece of paper in the world. A molecule of chocolate cake or ice cream would be the smallest piece of chocolate cake or ice cream in the world. It would be far too small to see and even if you could see it, it would soon fly into the air like smoke because the air molecules would bump it and bang it all over the place.

Suppose you could examine a single molecule of cake. Suppose you tried to cut it in half. What do you think would happen? Do you think you could have half a molecule of cake or ice cream or paper or anything else? You couldn't. It would be impossible. It would no longer be cake or ice cream or paper or anything else because it would fly apart and turn into gases. It would break up just as a clock might smash to pieces and all the wheels and springs fall out. The clock would no longer be a clock but would be a mass of cogwheels,

Atoms Are Like Letters

BY JEROME S. MEYER

Illustrated by
Charles Clement

screws, and springs that make it up. The same is true for the molecules in most of the things we see around us.

Now the question you naturally want to ask is: "If molecules are so small that nobody can see them, how can they break up into anything?" It is true that a molecule is so small that it is invisible and it is indeed hard to imagine how it can be made up of anything. But remember, a molecule is the smallest particle of a real thing and things are all different.

220

You know that a piece of paper is quite different from a stone; that a baseball is very different from strawberry jam; that a chocolate soda is not at all like a piece of wood. You know that you can bounce your rubber ball up and down and it won't break; but if you tried this with a goldfish bowl, it would smash to pieces. What makes these differences in things? Why does rubber stretch so easily and why does glass break so easily? Why can you see through glass and can't see through iron?

The answer to all these questions and many more like them is that the molecules that make up different things are different. What a thing is like—whether it stretches and bounces like a rubber band or a rubber ball, or whether it is brittle like a cup and saucer, whether it is soft like cotton or hard like iron or steel—depends upon the make-up and arrangement of the molecules in that thing. Often the arrangement of the molecules in a thing is very important in determining what it will be like. A piece of coal has the same molecules in it as a diamond yet see how different they are—just because the molecules are arranged differently in coal from the way they are in a diamond. And there are millions and millions of different molecules too.

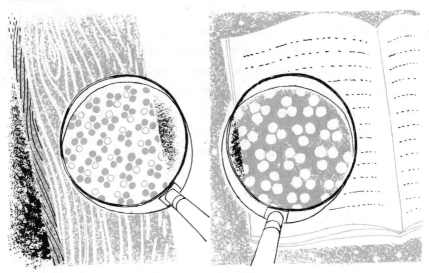

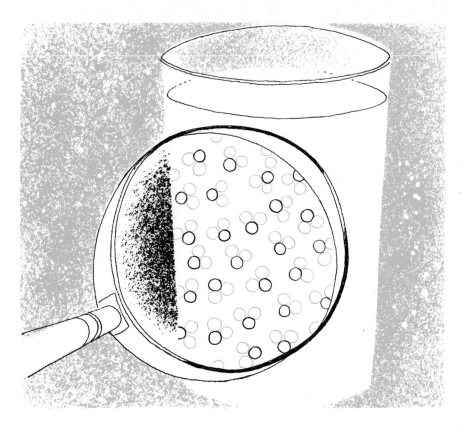

ATOM is another very important word. It is just as important as molecule.

Atoms make up molecules and molecules make up everything in this world. A molecule of paper is composed of different atoms than a molecule of stone. That's why paper and stone are so different. A molecule of wood is composed of different atoms than a molecule of soda pop. That is why wood and soda pop are so different. That is why there are so many millions of different things in this world.

Suppose you could make yourself so small that you could crawl inside of a tiny drop of water. Now suppose you had some kind of magic eyeglasses which could see the molecules in that tiny drop of water. And suppose that these magic eye-

222

glasses not only could show you the molecules but they also could enable you to see the atoms that make up the molecules. Of course all this would be impossible but just suppose it were possible. What would you see? If you looked carefully you would see that each water molecule contains two atoms that look exactly alike and one atom that looks quite different. Every molecule that you examine while in that tiny drop of water would be just the same. It would contain two atoms that are exactly alike and one atom that looks different. After examining millions and millions of these molecules you would naturally say that the water molecule is made up of three atoms: two alike and one different. The two of one kind are called H and one of another kind is called O. We shall see what the H and O stand for later on.

If you could crawl inside of a tiny piece of paper you would see quite a different picture, for each molecule contains six atoms of one kind, ten atoms of another kind and five atoms of still another kind. Yes, twenty-one atoms make up the paper molecule. If you could see inside of a molecule of butter you would be looking at about one hundred and twenty atoms. There would be almost 40 atoms of Carbon, 75 atoms of Hydrogen and 4 atoms of Oxygen—all inside of the butter molecule. Think of this the next time you eat bread and butter and think how much more complicated it will get if you add sugar or strawberry jam.

It is almost impossible to picture a molecule or an atom. We know some molecules are larger than others. Some, like the rubber molecules, are quite long but exactly what they look like is very difficult to describe. In most things it is the number of atoms and the kind of atoms in a molecule that make it different from other molecules.

Atoms Are Like Letters—
Molecules Are Like Words

All the words in our language are made up of letters from the alphabet. The word BOY, for example, is made up of three letters, B, O and Y. If you put these three different letters together in that order you will get the word BOY and if you arrange them in any other way you won't get any word at all. You may have learned this when you played with your ABC blocks years ago. Now, if instead of B you choose another letter like T to go with OY, you get a new word TOY which is quite different from the word BOY. So from only 26 different letters in our alphabet, you can make hundreds of thousands of different words just by arranging the letters in different ways. Yes, only 26 letters make hundreds of thousands of different words! Notice also that the letters are always the same no matter what words they are in. An A is always

an A whether it is in MARY or LAMB. It never changes. This is true for all the other letters in the alphabet.

Just as we make hundreds of thousands of words from only 26 letters, so Nature makes millions and millions of different things from only 92 different atoms. These 92 different atoms are Nature's alphabet. She uses them to make everything we see or hear or touch or smell. She combines them in millions of different ways to form molecules, just as we combine letters in different ways to make our words.

EARLY in the century, William Wallace had invented an electric arc lamp. This light hissed loudly as it glowed. The carbon sticks burned out quickly and had to be replaced every few hours. The Wallace arc gave off so much heat and such bad odors that it could not be used for indoor lighting. Surely, thought Edison, electricity could produce a cheap, easy and safe light. In March, 1878, he began working to make electricity give a softer, brighter and more efficient light than that produced by the Wallace electric arc.

To obtain the privacy he needed for his new experiments, Edison closed Menlo Park to the public. A reporter for the *New York Sun* visited the inventor to learn why he no longer permitted visitors. To this young man Edison confessed he planned to invent an electric light which would make no noise and produce no smell. It would create no smoke. It would be so safe that a child could carry it upside down from place to place.

New Light for the World

BY G. GLENWOOD CLARK

Illustrated by Seymour Fleishman

"How long will it take you to invent your new light?" asked the reporter.

"Well," said Edison slowly, "I figure it will take me about two years to get everything worked out. You see, I must keep all bugs out of my new light."

"Bugs in the electric light!" gasped the reporter. "What do you mean, sir?"

"By bugs I mean defects," explained Edison smiling. "I must produce an electric light that will have no faults. My light will be perfect before I give it to the world."

225

The reporter hastened back to New York City and printed his story in the *Sun*. The world's most famous electrical experts jeered at the magic light that Edison promised to invent. They declared that electric current could never be tamed and forced to light a small lamp for home or office use.

The Wizard of Menlo Park paid no attention to the experts; he worked night and day in his laboratory to do what others said could not be done.

Taking a hint from the Wallace arc lights, Edison decided to produce his new light by heating a substance to white heat. He experimented with thin loops of metal and other materials. These loops he called filaments. He soon made one important discovery: all his filaments burned to ashes in a few moments when they were heated in the open air.

In April, 1879, Edison had an inspiration. What would happen if he enclosed the filament inside a glass globe that contained no air? He determined to find out. Edison employed Ludwig Boehm, a Philadelphia glass blower, to come to Menlo Park and blow glass globes. An air pump could pump the air out of the globes. Only one air pump powerful enough for this purpose existed in the United States. It belonged to Princeton University, but Edison got that pump and installed it in the Menlo Park laboratory.

Francis Jehl, a new office boy, became special attendant to the air pump. Hundreds and hundreds of times, Edison wired a filament inside a hollow glass globe, attached the globe to the air pump and asked Frank Jehl to start the pump. When all the air had been drawn out of the glass bulb, the inventor turned electric current into the filament. When it became white-hot, the loop gave off a soft, bright light. In less than an hour, however, the glowing thread would turn to ash and the light would go out. Though they lasted longer than the old air-filled lamps, the vacuum lamps still did not last long enough. Edison knew he was on the right track. On April 12, 1879, he applied for a patent to cover his invention of the first vacuum lamp, even though it was imperfect.

At three o'clock on Sunday morning, October 19, 1879, Edison and Batchelor worked at a desk in the Menlo Park laboratory. Presently a heavy tread sounded on the stairway. Into the room came Alfred Swanson, the night watchman. He deposited a container of lampblack on the desk beside Batchelor.

"Here's the latest supply of lampblack, sir," he said.

"Thank you, Al," replied Batchelor. "I was waiting for it."

Edison walked over to Batchelor. In his hands, the inventor held a number of short lengths of white sewing thread. He had cut the strands himself with a pair of office scissors. He laid the threads before Batchelor.

"Let's get these filaments ready for cooking," he said. "Today I shall try a new experiment."

Batchelor spread out on a board the lampblack Swanson had just brought in. Taking a white thread, he placed it on the board and began to roll it back and forth in the lampblack. The cotton thread soaked up the greasy substance and became a sticky, black thread.

After he had blackened several threads, Batchelor gave them to Edison. The inventor took a small, fireproof tray and carefully lined it with tissue paper. Taking one of the blackened threads, he bent it gently into a horseshoe loop. This he placed on the paper bed. Beside it he laid other threads. Over these, he smoothed a second layer of tissue paper. Finally, he put the smaller tray into a larger one.

"Now, we'll put this into the furnace," he said.

Edison baked the neatly packed container in a hot furnace for several hours. When he thought the threads had turned into charcoal, he removed the tray from the oven.

"I'm going to get a wink of sleep while the filaments cool," remarked Edison. "Why don't you do the same, Batchelor?"

The inventor picked up two heavy books from his desk and walked down the laboratory until he found a clear space. Using his books to form a pillow, Edison stretched out on the hard, wooden floor and instantly fell asleep. Batchelor settled himself in a chair. In a few moments he, too, was asleep.

At six o'clock, Edison awoke, greatly refreshed by his nap. Carefully he unpacked the cool tray. The cooking had changed the cotton threads into loops of pure charcoal. He inserted a black filament in a glass globe without breaking the thin little loop. By this time Batchelor awoke. He attached stems to the filament and placed the glass globe in the air pump.

"That'll do for a bit," said Edison. "Frank will soon be here

228

with a breakfast tray for me. You'd better go and get your own breakfast."

As Edison spoke, Frank Jehl entered with hot food from Mrs. Edison's kitchen. The lad placed the tray before the inventor and went about his morning task of cleaning the laboratory. By the time he had completed this daily chore, Edison had finished his meal.

"Don't bother to take the tray back now," ordered Edison. "I need you here."

"Yes, sir," replied Frank. "What shall I do?"

"Start the air pump, my boy. I'm either on the edge of a great triumph or of a failure that will mean more hard work for all of us."

Frank climbed upon his stool beside the pump and opened a valve. The machine began to draw air from the glass bulb that Batchelor had earlier attached to it.

"Turn off the valve, Frank," ordered Edison after a few moments. The boy turned a stopcock.

The inventor pulled a switch to let a small electric current flow into the bulb. The filament turned a faint red. In silence both man and boy watched the dull glow.

"You see," Edison explained presently, "all of the vacuum bulbs before this one failed to burn more than a few minutes. They were not the complete vacuums we thought them. When the full current was turned on, the heat expelled the air imprisoned in the charcoal cells. This new air filled the bulb, spoiled the vacuum and caused the filament to burn out. This time, I am heating the filament a second time to drive off all the air that might be in it. In a minute I shall turn off the current, start the air pump again and draw off any air that may be in the globe. This second pumping should give me a perfect vacuum—and the lamp I need."

A few seconds later Edison shut off the electric current. The filament went cold and dark. "Start the pump again, Frank," said Edison. "Now we'll see how my new experiment turns out."

Frank opened the stopcock and the air pump began its work.

Up the stairs came Ludwig Boehm, the glass blower. "Boss," he said in his thick, foreign accent, "I want today a vacation. I go to New York City for the day. I will be back by six o'clock this night."

"All right, Boehm," replied Edison. "But, before you go, I want you to blow some extra globes. I may need them before the day ends."

Boehm went away. After a time Edison ordered Frank to cut off the air pump.

"Now we must learn how long this new type of vacuum globe will burn," remarked the inventor. He turned a switch.

230

The black filament inside the bulb began to glow faintly. A moment later Edison advanced the switch to its full extent. The filament grew white hot and sent out a warm, clear light, brilliant even in the morning sunshine that now streamed in through the laboratory windows.

Boehm soon returned with a supply of freshly blown globes. He placed these on the work table and, with a new promise to be back at Menlo Park by six o'clock, hurried off to catch his train to New York.

Edison and Frank watched the gleaming light. Fifteen minutes passed, then an hour. By twelve o'clock, the light had burned nearly four hours—the longest time any lamp had ever burned in the laboratory. Frank felt his heart thumping. Had the Boss created the perfect lamp he had worked so long to get?

As the afternoon wore on and the light continued to shed its soft radiance, Edison refused to leave the laboratory. Frank brought him a late lunch on a tray.

"You've been on duty a long time, my boy," said the inventor. "You'd better go home and rest."

"Let me stay, Mr. Edison," begged Frank. "I want to watch with you."

Edison smiled at his young assistant. "If you really want to remain, you may stay and help me watch."

At six o'clock that afternoon, Ludwig Boehm returned from New York City. Edison asked him to seal off the globe while it burned on the tube of the air pump. A few skillful movements of Boehm's expert fingers sealed off the lamp. It was now a glass-enclosed vacuum attached only to its wires.

A hum of delight swept through the little group of watching men when the clock struck eight. The light had burned continuously for twelve hours. Kind voices now suggested that

Edison go home and sleep while his employees kept watch. Edison refused to leave. He would himself keep guard through the night. Frank Jehl begged to share the inventor's watch. Remembering the hundreds of bulbs that the boy had pumped empty of air, and wishing his faithful worker to be present at what might prove to be the successful creation of the world's first electric lamp, Edison agreed to let Frank watch with him.

At midnight Mrs. Edison sent in a tray of food. In the glow of the lamp that still burned triumphantly, Edison and Frank shared a midnight feast. Several times during the long, dark hours, Kreusi, Boehm or Lawson dropped in for a few minutes. The lamp still lived and glowed.

When the clock struck eight on the morning of Monday, October 20, the wondrous lamp had burned for twenty-four hours. Tired and sleepy, Edison and Frank went to their homes for a nap. Batchelor and others took up the watch. They promised to note the exact minute and second the light burned out.

Monday night, Edison and Frank returned to the laboratory. The lamp still lived! Batchelor and his assistants refused to leave the room. Mrs. Sally Jordan sent food from her boarding house for them. To keep themselves awake, the watchers told jokes and sang. Even as they joked and sang, their eyes turned again and again to the shining glass globe. Edison's head ached from his constant staring at the glowing filament inside the lamp. To ease his throbbing temples, he seated himself at the pipe organ in the laboratory and picked out tunes with one finger.

At sunrise on Tuesday, October 21, 1879, the pioneer lamp still burned. Every worker who could leave his post crowded into the laboratory. Between one and two o'clock on that Tuesday afternoon, Edison knew that he had created a lamp that would burn indefinitely. To learn more about this magic

232

lamp he now decided to destroy it. While men held their breaths, the creator of the electric light placed his hand on the switch that controlled the current flowing into the globe. Notch by notch, the inventor fed more and more current into the bulb. The filament glowed brighter and brighter. There was a sudden flash . . . and the lamp went dead. Edison removed the ruined globe and sent it at once to be examined under the microscope.

The electric light was born on that Tuesday, October 21, 1879, when Edison produced the first long-burning vacuum bulb. Proud of his accomplishment, the inventor asked the editor of the *New York Herald* to send a reporter to Menlo Park. Marshall Fox and a newspaper artist hurried to Edison's workshop. For two weeks, under the guidance of laboratory employees, the reporter and the illustrator worked together. On Sunday, December 21, 1879, the *Herald* published the story of the invention of the electric light.

OF all the men who were alive when America was young, Ben Franklin would be the most at home if he could come back here today. More than a hundred and seventy years ago he wrote: "The rapid progress true science makes occasions my regretting sometimes that I was born so soon. It is impossible to imagine the height to which may be carried, in a thousand years, the power of men over matter."

Ben wouldn't be at all surprised to see airplanes flying across land and sea, and washing machines washing clothes, and penicillin curing people of their illnesses.

You could not name anything that Benjamin Franklin wasn't interested in. He was not only interested in what was going to happen in the future. He also thought about ways of improving the lives of the people who were living in his own time.

The very cold winter weather of Philadelphia was one subject to which he gave thought. Sometimes when he sat in front of his smoky fireplace, burning his face and knees while his back was left to freeze, it seemed to him that it was time to improve heating systems. He had noticed that heated air rises and cold air rushes in to take its place. Fireplaces of that day, with small openings and more drafts than heat, did not take advantage of this fact. So he worked out the plan for an open stove that gave out more heat and used less fuel.

Franklin put this stove in his own house. He soon found

Ben Franklin of Old Philadelphia

BY
MARGARET COUSINS

Illustrated by
Fritz Eichenberg

234

that his family—especially the women, who were apt to stay at home and sit by the fire—got fewer colds and not so many toothaches.

One of his good friends, Robert Grace, had an iron foundry and Ben showed him a model of the stove.

"Why don't you go to work and make up some of these to sell to the people?" Ben said. "I've been using this contraption in my common room and it is twice as warm as it used to be for one-quarter of the wood I used to burn there."

"I can make it, but how can I sell it?" Robert Grace asked. "I'm just an ironmonger."

"I'll put a piece in the *Gazette* about it," Ben said.

He sat down and wrote a long description of the stove. The article began by saying how much more comfortable the stove could make a room, and how the big fires people had to have in fireplaces to keep warm, dried out their skins, dulled their eyes, and made them look old. With the Franklin stove, he went on, this didn't have to happen. (This made every woman in Philadelphia want a Franklin stove!)

In the rest of the article he explained the way the stove worked so that men could understand it. To this he added a list of its advantages and answered in advance any objections that might come up. He then gave complete instructions for installing the stove in any fireplace.

As a further aid to Robert Grace, whose iron works was in Chester County, not in Philadelphia proper, Franklin put in a stock of stoves at the post office, where he was postmaster.

Then he published his article in a pamphlet, instead of in the *Gazette,* and began to circulate it. The pamphlet excited plenty of interest and Governor Thomas, who was then head of the Colony of Pennsylvania, offered Ben a patent which would prevent anybody else from selling it.

Ben refused. He said: "As we enjoy great advantages from

235

the invention of others, we should be glad of an opportunity to serve others by any invention of ours."

The Franklin stove was the first improvement in heating in many long years. People were delighted to have heat that made them more comfortable and was less expensive at the same time. Franklin stoves were soon in style, and shortly they came into general use. (You can still see Franklin stoves today.) They undoubtedly improved the health of the colonists and influenced the design of stoves for years to come. They were much admired in Europe and copied in England. History notes that two were sent as presents to Leopold, Grand Duke of Tuscany.

Ben never lost his interest in better heating. He liked comfort and was always poking his nose up chimneys to see whether or not something couldn't be done to make them work better. He wrote a long letter on *The Cause and Cure of Smoky Chimneys* to one of his scientist friends after he became a very old man. During the winter of 1771, when he was living in London, he invented a new stove for burning coal. He used his stove in London and later at home in Philadelphia; and when he went to France as Ambassador he took it along.

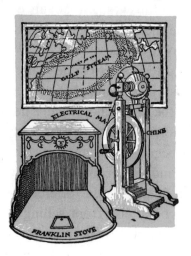

ON THE afternoon of June 24, 1876, Alexander Graham Bell walked through the Centennial Fair Grounds at Fairmount Park in Philadelphia. The model of the telephone had been sent on ahead. It was extremely hot, as Philadelphia often is at the end of June, and the bag that he carried seemed heavier than when he left Boston. He had had a long uncomfortable journey and had taken time for only a cup of tea and a bun in the station in order that he might get to the Centennial Exposition before it closed for the day. He had been informed that the judges would inspect his telephone on Sunday morning, which was next day.

Arranging the instruments did not take him long. The models that had been made especially for the exposition were soon in order.

Next morning Willie Hubbard, his wife's cousin, arrived, and together they went back to the East Gallery. Only exhibitors were allowed on Sunday morning. They did not even have to show passes. The great hall was very quiet when they entered. Here and there an exhibitor was making some last-minute adjustment in the things he had to show, but most of them sat idly waiting or chatting together.

Mr. Bell Invents the Telephone

BY KATHERINE B. SHIPPEN

Illustrated by Serge Hollerbach

Bell could think of nothing more that he could do with his instrument, so he and Willie Hubbard sat down in chairs beside it and waited. After a long time a bell sounded in the distance. At the far end of the hall a door was thrown open, and the judges entered in their stovepipe hats and long frock coats.

237

Bell and Willie Hubbard watched them across the wide spaces of the hall. Slowly, with long pauses before each exhibit, they came nearer. "That must be Lord Kelvin," Willie said excitedly. "The greatest scientist in the world today, they say he is. What a man for a judge!" Willie had been well posted on all the notables.

"And who do you suppose that can be with him?" Willie asked. "That heavy man with the reddish hair and the square-cut beard?"

Bell peered across the hall. "Why, I know him," he said. "I've talked to him. He came up to the Boston School for the Deaf when I was teaching there. Wanted to know what methods we used. Talked a long time—or I did, rather." Bell smiled.

"But who is he?" Willie Hubbard asked, exasperated at all this talk when all he wanted was to be told a name.

"He comes from Brazil," Bell continued. "His name is Dom Pedro. He's the Emperor."

"Dom Pedro!" Willie said. "Why didn't you say so? He's the guest of honor of the whole Fair."

Now the judges had come to the exhibition of Swedish glass just beside the place where Bell and Willie Hubbard sat. They were so near that it was easy to hear what they were saying.

"Gentlemen," they heard Lord Kelvin speaking in his clear-cut aristocratic English voice, "if you will inspect this collection of glass from Sweden, we will pause in our considerations and continue with our judging tomorrow. This American heat makes it impossible—"

Bell looked at Willie Hubbard. "That's the end of that," he said. "Tomorrow I shall be on a train to Boston. I've got to get back and start teaching again. Maybe it's just as well."

238

The judges had inspected the Swedish glass—not too carefully perhaps. Lord Kelvin turned to leave the hall. He paused, and with customary ceremony, waited for the Emperor to precede him. But Dom Pedro, a man of curiosity and independence, did not turn immediately. He wanted to see what the small exhibit on the adjoining table might be. He stopped for a moment, and recognized Alexander Graham Bell, the pale face, the dark ruffled hair, the burning eyes.

"Why, Mr. Bell," he said. And in a moment he was striding toward him with outstretched hand. "How are things going in Boston?" he asked. "What is this you are showing here?"

Then Bell told him that he had brought a model of the telephone, and that he was sorry that it would not be judged, for it would be necessary for him to leave tomorrow. "I am sorry that the judges will not have an opportunity to see it," he said politely.

"But that's impossible," Dom Pedro said. "Of course they'll have to see it now. Lord Kelvin," he called, turning back to the impatient group of judges, "I must ask you to wait, gentlemen. This is Mr. Bell of Boston. He has made what he calls a telephone. He cannot wait until tomorrow to show it to us. We must see it now."

Wearily the judges turned. Even great scientists could not gainsay the request of the Emperor who was also the guest of honor of Philadelphia's Centennial.

"Will Mr. Bell demonstrate his telephone?" Lord Kelvin asked.

Aleck rose and, having nothing that seemed suitable to say, bowed. Willie Hubbard rose too, and turned to the instrument on the table.

Then Aleck walked to the transmitter which he had rigged

at the far end of the Exhibition Hall, took up the instrument, and waited for the familiar hum and click which meant that Willie Hubbard had turned on the current. "All right, Willie," he called into the transmitter.

"Mr. Bell has an invention here which he calls the telephone." The voice of Dom Pedro held the judges as if against their will. There was nothing to prevent their leaving, but not one of them turned away.

"His telephone is a device by which a human voice may be carried along an electric wire, so that a person standing at the other end of the wire may hear the speaker as if he stood beside him."

The judges made no comment. Some of them looked bored, and some incredulous. Some of them looked merely hot.

"It's ready," Willie said to the assembled gentlemen. "Your Majesty, will you begin?"

240

Dom Pedro stepped forward and took up the little metal box which Willie held out to him. "Hold it close to your ear," Willie said.

There was a moment's pause. Dom Pedro stood in rapt attention; the judges watched. Then suddenly a smile broke across his face, an expression of incredulous surprise. "My God, it talks!" he said.

Then Lord Kelvin took the instrument.

" 'To be, or not to be,' " he murmured, as if he were repeating the words of some priest in a great cathedral. " 'That is the question.' " He took the small black box down from his ear, looked at it, then raised it to his other ear, and listened. " 'The slings and arrows of outrageous fortune,' " he murmured. "Extraordinary! Will you try it, sir?"

A third judge stepped forward and took the small box attached to its wire and placed it to his ear. " 'By opposing end

them'—I can hear it quite plainly. There is no doubt about it."

One after another the judges forgot the heat, forgot that they wanted to go home. They passed the receiver from one to another, taking turns. It was a thing they had never dreamed would be possible—to hear a voice that came clear, well modulated from the far end of the Exhibition Hall, to hear every word, every syllable. "Remarkable," they kept saying. "Extraordinary."

"Let Lord Kelvin try talking," one of them said at last. "Let him see if he can make his voice come over the wire like that."

Lord Kelvin turned and walked away across the hall. After a period of about five minutes Professor Barker of the University of Pennsylvania took up the receiver. "Sir William is speaking," he said. "Listen, Your Majesty." And he passed the instrument to the red-haired Emperor.

Slowly, solemnly, in a low voice Dom Pedro repeated, " 'To be, or not to be'—It's Lord Kelvin's very voice."

The demonstration was soon over. Bell, with Lord Kelvin, came walking back to the little group of waiting judges. They clapped as they saw him approaching, then one after another they shook his hand.

"Remarkable! Extraordinary!" they kept saying to one another, as they made their way at last through the doors of the Exhibition Hall. Dom Pedro lingered a little after the others had gone.

"It's the most remarkable thing in America," he said. "You have made an invention that will change the way people live all over the world. There isn't any doubt about your getting the award, of course." He smiled at the confused young man. "Better get back to Boston," he said kindly. "You'll hear from us again."

Several days later the announcement of the award arrived.

242

With it came a letter from Lord Kelvin, and Bell read the words of the great scientist with what seemed like a quiver of electricity:

I need scarcely say I was astonished and delighted, as were others, including some other judges of our group, who witnessed the experiments and verified with their own ears the electric transmission of speech. This, perhaps the greatest marvel hitherto achieved by the electric telegraph, has been obtained by appliances of quite a homespun and rudimentary character. With somewhat more advanced plans and more powerful apparatus, we may confidently expect that Mr. Bell will give us the means of making voice and spoken words audible through the electric wire to an ear hundreds of miles distant.

"Rudimentary? Homespun?" said Mr. Watson later when Bell showed him the letter. His workmanship had been as good as any man could accomplish. "There wasn't anything homespun about it."

NOBODY is really sure which pioneering European printer finally invented movable type and worked out a satisfactory method of making and using it. Probably several men had some good ideas at about the same time, and slowly the ideas were put together.

Perhaps the first man who successfully used movable type was a Dutchman named Laurens Janszoon, who was a sexton or Koster in the town of Haarlem, and who is sometimes called Laurens Koster.

But more probably it was a German known as Johann Gutenberg, who was born in the town of Mainz in about the year 1397. Johann's real name was Gensfleisch, which means Goose Flesh. Apparently he didn't like it very well, because he always called himself by his mother's name, Gutenberg, which means Good Mountain.

Gutenberg borrowed money to experiment with certain new "tools," as he called them. Experts believe that those "tools" may have been the first satisfactory movable type in Europe.

Johann Gutenberg and His Type

BY SAM AND BERYL EPSTEIN

Illustrated by Ezra Jack Keats

Probably Gutenberg hired a skilled metalworker to cut each letter of the alphabet in relief on the end of a small stick, or punch. This punch was then used to press the shape of each letter into a small square of metal. The letter-shaped hollow made by the punch was what printers called a *matrix*. When Gutenberg had a matrix for each letter of the alphabet, he

244

could make his type, making A's from the A matrix, B's from the B matrix, and so on.

In order to make pieces of type of the letter A he fitted four pieces of wood around the A matrix in such a way that the matrix formed the bottom of a tiny open box. If he looked down into the box he could see the shape of the letter A hollowed out on the floor. At the top of the box was a funnel.

Gutenberg poured hot melted metal through the funnel into the box, first letting it fill up the letter-shaped mold at the bottom and then pouring in more metal until the box was filled right to the top. After the metal cooled and hardened, he removed the sides of the box and picked up the metal. It was in the shape of a tiny block with the letter A in relief on its underside.

Afterward Gutenberg could put the box back together again and cast several more pieces of type of the letter A. And

when he had made as many A's as he needed, he could rebuild the little box, this time around the B matrix, and cast as many pieces of type of B as he needed.

The movable walls of the little box in which Gutenberg made his type formed a mold that is called an *adjustable type mold,* because it could be adjusted to fit all letters. The invention of this mold was an important step forward in the development of a quicker and cheaper method of printing.

Gutenberg discovered that the best metal to use for his type was a mixture of lead and tin and antimony. This metal didn't shrink when it cooled, so he could be sure that all his letters would be exactly like the original matrix, and that his pieces of type would fit neatly together in snug rows. This mixture of lead and tin and antimony is still used for the making of type today. It is called *type metal.*

 IT TOOK John James Audubon and his bride, Lucy, twelve days by carriage and flatboat, through wildly beautiful country, to make the trip to Louisville. Louisville was their choice because young Audubon had already explored the territory and had decided that the people and surroundings would make settling in Louisville a pleasant and profitable business.

Poor Audubon! Things always looked rosy to him until the bills started coming in. And even then, tomorrow was another day. He did not change when he opened the store in Louisville. When things looked black, he was sure the next day would bring good sales of grain and cutlery and shot pouches and fruit. In the meantime, the woods were always inviting.

And then, of course, there were the times he did portraits of young ladies in order to earn enough money to buy food for his family.

Then, without warning, on a cool March day in 1810 something happened that influenced the whole course of their lives —a sandy-haired Scot turned up in town.

John James Audubon

BY MARGARET AND JOHN KIERAN

Illustrated by Herbert Danska

His name was Wilson . . . Alexander Wilson . . . and by the oddest kind of coincidence he had hit, some years earlier, upon the idea of drawing all the birds of North America. Indeed, the first volume of the Wilson series had already been published.

He and Audubon had never met but now, dramatically,

247

their paths crossed. They compared drawings, exchanged some natural history information, and parted. Wilson was no doubt annoyed that he was no longer the only one in the field, and Audubon himself felt a bit surprised at finding he had a rival.

The meeting was a very brief one . . . Wilson stayed in town only a few days. Yet it was important because of the fact that Audubon was becoming more and more convinced that his great work was to be the publication of *life-size paintings of every North American bird*. This was an even more ambitious project than the one Wilson was undertaking.

As usual, Lucy was right by her husband's side with encouraging words.

"You can do it," she told him excitedly. "You have great talent and great energy. You were not meant to be a shopkeeper. You must keep getting more specimens. *You must keep painting*."

This was what he wanted to hear, and he was off the next day at sunrise and many, many days after that. Even his deep affection for their first child, Victor, born a year before in 1809, did not distract him.

Sometimes as he lay quietly in the woods waiting for a warbler to appear, he felt like a little boy again at Nantes. It almost seemed as if he could hear his stepmother calling: "Come home, Fougère! It is time for supper."

But the birds were different here. Such variety, such color, and so many of them! The Audubons were living in a wonderful section for watching the birds travel north and south, and soon the young naturalist's portfolio was bulging with water colors, pastels and rough pencil sketches of every bird he could discover.

"How do you know what kind of branch to put in as a background for the oriole?" Lucy asked her husband one day as he sat outside the house, his water colors at hand, his sketch pad as usual before him.

"I watch, my dear," he replied. "I watch closely every minute of my time in the woods. There is nothing that I do not notice. The day is not long enough when I am close to nature. Never have I seen such birds as are around Louisville. All of them are not known to me, by any means. The warblers dazzle me in the spring and confuse me in the fall. *But I will draw them.*"

He told her of the black-crowned night herons and the wood ducks that looked almost like painted toys. He told her too about the sound of a bittern that he first thought was an old-time wooden pump. There were woodpeckers and barred owls. There were all the birds that are familiar to us today, birds we can see in his famous paintings as well as on the Audubon charts that are printed in his memory.

Lucy sat mending a woolen sock as he poured out to her the adventures he had had in the woods.

It was not enough, you see, for him to observe the birds, to see them feeding or preening or soaring above him. He must

249

know just exactly how the feathers folded, one above the other, how the wings lay close to the bodies, how the beaks were formed.

During these days there were the usual business reverses which once became so serious that Lucy was obliged to take a position as governess.

Never mind, they would eat! And Audubon could go on painting.

That is why his gun was always by his side. To capture the actual bird, to put it on his drawing board and to measure every feature, that was what excited him most. The ambition to paint the full life-size series of every bird of America had seized his imagination so that he could think of little else.

For too long he had been dabbling in painting and woodsy daydreaming. For too long he had seen the reproachful looks of his family as he proved that he was not a businessman. Now,

at last, he set his jaw and made a resolution. Nothing would stop him from becoming great.

From this time on the story of Audubon's life is a really thrilling tale of singleness of purpose. There were no hardships too extreme for him . . . walking miles in his bare feet when his shoes had worn out, tramping in rain-drenched fields, or wading through stagnant swamps. All these inconveniences were as nothing if he came back with his booty. Maybe it would be an indigo bunting, that true-blue songster that he painted with such love. Maybe it would be the huge wild turkey, one of the most famous of his magnificent series.

Whatever the specimen, Lucy was happy when she saw him returning with it. Busy over a huge kettle in the kitchen, she breathed a prayer of thanks that he would be occupied the next day, feverishly at work on a sketch and later a painting.

"If I were jealous I should have a bitter time of it, for

251

every bird is my rival," Lucy wrote to her sister one day when her husband was miles away on a hunting trip.

A hunting trip meant that he was hunting birds, of course, because by this time Audubon was like a man on fire. He thought of nothing but his Great Work. Lucy had to remind him when meals were ready or he would have stayed over his drawing board day and night, painting, tearing up that painting, starting another, making corrections. Then finally he could put the huge sheet of paper away until another day.

Like any true artist he was never satisfied with the finished product.

"The Blackburnian warbler I did at Fatland Ford," he said, "I must work over a little. The bird is not so bad, but the flowers . . . the phlox . . . can stand a little polishing. They are too stiff as I have them now painted."

He held it away from him.

Lucy did not agree. "It is very delicate," she said. "I can almost smell the perfume."

"But see," he pointed out, "here the outline should be a little less sharp so that the bird will stand out."

She nodded and watched him proudly as he worked painstakingly over every tiny detail.

He had made great strides in his drawing technique. And remember that he was practically self-taught. He had to work out his own problems with no teacher at his side to help smooth the way.

At first he was chiefly concerned with obtaining an accurate likeness of the bird . . . the exact size, the exact colors, the exact position in flight or at rest. For this he sometimes had to wait months because he needed not only the male bird from which to work but the female and often the young as well. Occasionally he would take a dead bird apart to see just how

252

the head and jaw were constructed, so that each line he drew would be true to nature.

What fascinated him almost more than anything else was the task of getting a life-like expression in the eyes . . . that frightened and suspicious look a bird has when human beings come near. This Audubon did by sharp highlights, a trick he could have learned at art school, no doubt, but one that he had nevertheless developed alone.

After he was sure that his drawing was accurate, he went on with the task of arranging the bird and the background in an artistic composition. It was not enough to copy nature, he must at times improve upon it.

Look at his painting of the pileated woodpecker, that bold and beautiful bird whose bill *rat-tat-ting* against a tree sounds like a man chopping wood. He pictured these birds against a

This is the painting of a pileated woodpecker by John James Audubon

background of wild grapes. The rich purple-blue of the fruit makes a lovely contrast for the red crests on the birds' heads.

By this time he had learned to paint the wood of trees in that soft brown tone he knew so well from daily observation. Backgrounds, too . . . soft fleecy clouds or distant hills . . . were no longer the difficult subjects they had once been.

All those days of "wasted time" in the woods were beginning to show results.

People—at least a few—were looking at him with a little more respect. Instead of thinking of him as that happy-go-lucky Frenchman who would rather watch birds than count change, they called him "Mr. Audubon," or even "Mr. Audubon, the artist."

It had taken years of observation and notation, but now there was a chance that his work might become known. Each day, each week, and each month swelled that huge portfolio of paintings.

But what good would four hundred or more pictures of the birds of America be if he could not sell them? And how *could* he sell them? Who could afford to buy them?

He looked at Lucy, who was always at hand when a new problem came up. "I'll have to work as a merchant a little while longer," he told her, "and save enough to pay my way to Philadelphia. Surely there are men of taste and wealth there who would be interested in my paintings."

He would be astonished today, no doubt, if he could see the way his fame has spread not only through his exciting paintings but through the activities of the Audubon Society which makes his work live on. It labors constantly for the protection of birds as well as for the conservation of all wildlife.

254

THE voyage to the New World had lasted six weeks and three days.

Now, both below and above deck, there were long, animated discussions. Some of the passengers had been to America, some to Canada, some to both countries. It had been Daniel Muir's intention to strike out for Canada, a sparsely settled country of great natural wealth and scenic grandeur and with millions upon millions of fertile prairie acres stretching to the horizon. But after listening to the arguments for and against, he changed his mind. The American Midwest had everything that Canada had, he was told, with this advantage for one who wished to farm: the forest could be held at bay when once some acres had been cleared.

The Muirs started westward by train. At a stopover in Buffalo a grain dealer told Daniel Muir that most of the wheat he handled came from Wisconsin. So Muir and his children set out for Wisconsin. At Milwaukee it was decided to head for a little town

John Muir Comes to America

BY CHARLES NORMAN

Illustrated by Eleanor Mill

called Kingston, one hundred miles away. The question was how to get there with all the stuff they had brought along. Daniel Muir had taken no chances. Also, he could not have foreseen that there were many places in the United States where he could have purchased food and equipment. He had brought along an immense ironbound box in which were crammed old-fashioned beam scales and cast-iron counterweights, carpenter's tools, iron wedges, and other odds and

255

ends, making a total weight of four hundred pounds! At Buffalo he had added to the load by purchasing a big cast-iron stove and pots and pans, a scythe and cradle for cutting wheat, and provisions. But a bargain was soon struck with a farmer who had brought in a wagonload of wheat and was returning to Fort Winnebago, near Kingston. For thirty dollars he agreed to carry the Muirs and their belongings.

It was just after the spring thaw. The roads over the prairies were winding troughs of mud. They were stuck often.

"Never, never again," exclaimed the farmer over and over as he and Daniel Muir got out to put their shoulders to the wheels, "never, never again will I be tempted to try to haul such a cruel, heartbreaking, wagon-breaking, horse-killing load— no, not for a *hundred* dollars!"

John and David also helped, while Sarah Muir sat primly in the wagon. Covered with mud, and weary, they arrived at last in Kingston. While the children stayed behind in a rented room, Daniel Muir went reconnoitering. He returned to announce that he had found some fine land by the side of a lake, with sunny, open woods all around. It was only ten miles away. Three yoke of oxen were hitched to a big wagon, and once more the Muirs started on their trek, this time through springtime woods. "Haw!" shouted the driver, and "Gee!" and the boys were amazed to see the oxen, with a harness consisting only of a chain and a crooked piece of wood, march steadily forward, pulling their heavy load. Except for the trail through the woods, barely wide enough for the wagon, this was the forest primeval, in all the leafy glory of the burgeoning spring.

With the help of his nearest neighbors Daniel Muir built a shanty in one day. Then, as the light began to fade, John and David spied a blue jay's nest and quickly climbed the tree

256

to feast their eyes on the beautiful green eggs that were in it. The parent birds set up a screaming, but they had nothing to fear; John and David were only looking at the eggs—they had no intention of robbing the nest. They descended from the tree and ran along the hillside where the shanty stood, and soon found a bluebird's nest and then a woodpecker's nest. There were also frogs, snakes, and turtles in the creeks and springs.

They slept soundly that night. The next morning they had a surprise. Climbing the tree to get another look at the blue jays, they found the nest empty! John and David wondered, then and later, how the birds could have carried off their eggs, either in their bills or between their feet, without breaking them. They also wondered how they could be kept warm while another nest was building. John never learned the answer. Nor has any ornithologist.

The boys continued their explorations as often as they dared, for there was now much to do to make the shanty snug and homelike and to wrest a living from the soil, and their father's eye was always on them. They saw the birds that had

remained all through the winter—the black-bibbed chickadees and the droll nuthatches that descend from a tree with their heads down. Now came bluebirds, to build their knothole nests, robins standing with cocked heads as though to hear the worms gliding beneath the grass, the brown thrush or thrasher, thrashing in heaps of leaves to find food; bobolinks, redwing blackbirds, big meadow larks, Baltimore orioles, and the song sparrow with its speckled breast and sweet notes. Prairie chickens strolled nonchalantly about with their families in a circle around them, picking seeds and snapping up grasshoppers. High in the sky they saw the harrow-shaped flocks of the Canada gray goose and heard their honking. And then came a memorable day: John and David saw the first flock of passenger pigeons arrive at their farm. They were like a cloud; and because they have vanished like a cloud, not a single specimen remaining the world, John Muir's description of them may be of interest.

"The breast of the male is a fine rosy red," he wrote in *The Story of My Boyhood and Youth,* "the lower part of the neck behind and along the sides changing from the red of the breast to gold, emerald-green, and rich crimson. The general color of the upper parts is grayish blue, the under parts white. The extreme length of the bird is about seventeen inches; the finely modeled slender tail about eight inches, and extent of wings twenty-four inches. The females are scarcely less beautiful. 'Oh, what bonnie, bonnie birds!' we exclaimed over the first that fell into our hands. 'Oh, what colors! Look at their breasts, bonnie as roses, and at their necks aglow wi' every color just like the wonderfu' wood ducks. Oh, the bonnie, bonnie creatures, they beat a'! Where did they a' come fra, and where are they a gan? It's awfu' like a sin to kill them!" To this some smug, practical old sinner would remark: 'Aye,

it's a peety, as ye say, to kill the bonnie things, but they were made to be killed, and sent for us to eat.' "

They were "made to be killed," and they were killed. Millions of them roosted in certain forests to rest and rear their young, with so many nests in every tree that branches sagged or broke. Soon, farmers learned of their stopping places in the woods and converged on them and beat the nests to the ground, clubbing to death the young and old birds and then driving in their hogs to fatten on the carcasses. Muir afterward recalled: "I have seen flocks streaming south in the fall so large that they were flowing over from horizon to horizon in an almost continuous stream all day long, at the rate of forty or fifty miles an hour, like a mighty river in the sky, widening, contracting, descending like falls and cataracts, and rising suddenly here and there in huge ragged masses like high-plashing spray."

Today not one remains.

Daniel Muir was stern, in a dour Scots sort of way, but he was a man of his word. Back home in Scotland he had promised John and David a pony ride in America, and it took only a few reminders from the boys for him to keep his promise. While in Kingston on business he purchased from a storekeeper,

259

for thirteen dollars, an Indian pony. The storekeeper got him in trade from a Winnebago Indian. The pony was a stout handsome bay two years old, with a long black mane and tail.

One day, to their surprise, their father said: "Noo, bairns, rin down the meadow and get your powny and learn to ride him."

The boys led Jack, as they had named the pony, to a smooth place near an Indian mound back of the house. John was the first to mount. He had crossed the mound and was at a slow walk along a wagon track when his father shouted, "Whup him up, John, whup him up! Make him gallop; gallopin' is easier and better than walkin' or trottin'."

Jack responded, and off they went at a good gallop, John holding on for dear life to the pony's mane. John cried, "Whoa, Jack!" and the pony stopped so suddenly that John flew over his head. The pony just stood there, as though thinking, "If that's the way you dismount, I'll get used to it, I suppose." John mounted him again and galloped back. Again he cried: "Whoa!" and again he went right over Jack's head, right into his father's arms. David's performance was no better. But after a month or so of practice both boys became skillful riders, without saddle or bridle. One of their favorite places was a so-called "kettle" on the Muir farm.

These kettles had been formed thousands of years before by the melting of huge blocks of ice buried in the soil, which formed hopper-shaped hollows. The one the boys rode in was about eighty feet wide and thirty feet deep. As they rode in, they went over Jack's head; as they rode out, they slid down Jack's tail.

Once John tried to teach Jack to jump a creek in the meadow at a point where it was about twelve feet across. Jack jumped bravely enough, with John on his back, but came down about midway. Although the water was only a foot deep, there

260

was a muddy bottom, into which Jack sank. John managed to clamber ashore, and was terrified on looking back to see his pony almost entirely out of sight, with only his head showing. He ran to call his father, who tied a long hemp rope—which he had brought from Scotland—around the pony's neck and hitched it to an ox team. Even so, getting the animal ashore was hard work. When Jack was on dry land at last, Daniel Muir turned to John.

"You should be ashamed," he said, "asking the puir beast to jump intil sic a saft bottomless place."

Although their father told them that all Jack needed was good meadow hay, the boys fed him corn as well, and he grew sleek and fat.

In the fall the frame house was finished, and the rest of the family came from Scotland. John, David, and Sarah were happily and noisily reunited with Margaret, Daniel, Mary, and Anna. (Later another sister, Joanna, was born in Wisconsin.) The oak shanty was converted into a stable for Jack.

After being under the strict rule and stern gaze of their father so long, the presence of their mother was like balm for the three children who had accompanied Daniel Muir to the New World. Mrs. Muir was quiet, affectionate, and fond of painting and poetry. It was probably from her that John inherited his sensitivity and imagination; and it was to her that he brought the tales of his adventures in the Wisconsin woods, and the new flowers and birds that came into his ken.

But his father was still a force to be reckoned with.

One mid-winter day Daniel Muir found John and David in the stable with Jack—and his ready anger burst on them like a storm. The two boys, having observed that Jack's hair was full of dust, had decided to give him a bath. Unfortunately they had failed to rub him dry, and soon a row of icicles formed under his belly. At that moment their father walked in. The

261

sight of the pony bespangled with ice pendants infuriated him.

"You ought to be ashamed o' yourseelves," he exclaimed, "soaking the puir beast in cauld water at this time o' year."

But instead of a thrashing, which both were sure they would get, he gave them some good advice: to use the brush and currycomb, not water.

Jack hadn't complained. The Indians had trained him to accept any situation with composure.

That winter, Indians from the Menominee or Winnebago tribes came to the farm for bread, matches, or to sharpen their knives on the Muir grindstone, and John and David kept a watchful eye on them for fear their pony would be stolen. Sometimes the boys were astonished to see the Indians go directly to some tree on the farm, chop a hole in it with their tomahawks, and drag out a terrified raccoon. They seemed to have a sixth sense about animals. After the first snow they saw them, running three and four together, tracking down deer— never stopping, never tiring, and at last catching up with their quarry.

Although John Muir was to win world-wide fame as a naturalist, it was not until his late twenties that he decided on his life's work. Until then it was a toss-up whether he would pursue his love of the wilderness and the outdoors or settle down to the more secluded life of an inventor.

The wording of the degree of Doctor of Laws he received years later may stand as his epitaph:

"John Muir, Born in Scotland, reared in the University of Wisconsin, by final choice a Californian, Widely travelled Observer of the world we dwell in, Man of Science and of Letters, Friend and Protector of Nature, Uniquely gifted to Interpret unto others Her mind and ways."

262

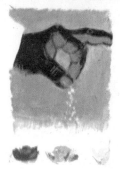

LONG ago when he was a child with Aunt Sue, George Carver had planted flowers close together to see if they would mix. Later on he had learned that bees do the mixing by carrying pollen from flower to flower. When he found that he himself could do the work of bees, a new world had opened for him.

He worked mostly with flowers that spring from bulbs. That was because in those days he was always on the move and could carry the bulbs from place to place in his pocket. Amaryllis was his pet. Everywhere he went, the rosy amaryllis went with him. He developed many varieties. One was a pure white. One was ten inches across.

In Iowa he went from flowers to fruit, creating new varieties of apples, pears, plums. By the time he left for the South, he was one of the best plant breeders in the world.

Plant Peanuts

BY ANNE TERRY WHITE

Illustrated by Ernest Crichlow

What would he breed at Tuskegee?.

"No matter what I do," Carver said to himself, "a large part of the farmers' crop will be cotton. At least I can give them a good variety to grow. They don't have to keep on planting cotton that bears just two bolls on a stalk."

So he planted and cross-bred cotton. Year after year he worked to develop kinds that would have more and bigger bolls on each plant. By 1909 he had created four new varieties. One had bolls of enormous size—275 of them on a single bush. The yield was nearly a bale and a quarter an acre.

The farmers of Macon County couldn't believe their ears when they heard about that cotton. How was it possible? Here

they had been planting cotton all their lives and all they could raise was a third of a bale on an acre. And this man Carver had never even seen cotton growing till he came to Tuskegee. The whole county, white folk and black, talked about the cotton up at Tuskegee.

The thing that puzzled the white planters most was that a Negro had raised it.

An important visitor from Germany got so excited about the cotton that he asked for three graduates from Tuskegee to go to the West Coast of Africa and show the people in the German colonies how to grow cotton. A visitor from Australia carried away seeds so he could introduce the cotton into his own country.

Carver took it in his stride. He had been doing this sort of thing all his life. What was so wonderful about it? He had done with cotton no more than he had done with amaryllis.

"People are making too much fuss about this cotton," Carver told Booker T. Washington, principal of Tuskegee University. "I would be better pleased if I could get the farmers to plant some crop besides cotton."

264

"You are doing it," the principal said. "A lot of our people are raising vegetables now. I see vegetable gardens and chickens all over Macon County. Our people are living better. They are eating better. There is less sickness."

"Well, yes, I know that," Carver said. "The other day I walked in on a farm family when they weren't expecting me. They were just sitting down to supper, and, of course, they asked me to eat with them. I remember when that family used to eat nothing but the three M's—meat, meal, and molasses. Now they 'live at home.' We had ham that was raised on the place, home-made butter, eggs, two kinds of canned fruit, and biscuits with syrup. The flour had been bought with egg money."

"A right good supper."

"It was. But 'living at home' doesn't take much land. And as long as most of it stays in cotton, the South will remain poor."

They were both thoughtful a moment. Then Washington said, "In a way, you can't blame the Negro farmers. Most of them don't own their land—they *have* to plant what the plantation owner says."

"That's very true," Carver agreed. "And look how the thing works out. If the farmers have a good crop, the price of cotton goes down and they don't make any money. If the weather is bad, they lose everything. . . . I am looking for some native plant they can grow and sell instead of cotton."

"You have been working with the sweet potato, I know."

"The sweet potato had a lot of possibilities," Carver answered. "When we first started growing it, we got forty bushels from an acre. Now the forty bushels have jumped to 266. We can get more bushels of sweet potatoes out of an acre of land than we can of any other crop. With care we can raise two

265

crops a year. They're easy to grow. And the wonderful part of it is that sweet potatoes do less harm to the soil than anything else. They get almost all their nourishment from the air."

"Then you think the answer to the cotton problem is sweet potatoes?"

"I don't know. Sweet potatoes don't keep well," said Carver. "But one thing is sure—help must come from somewhere, and right quick. Pretty soon the cotton farmer is going to have a worse enemy than weather. The Mexican boll weevil is heading this way. It was already in Texas when I came here. Now it is eating its way through Louisiana and Mississippi. Once it gets to Alabama, there will be mighty little cotton left for our farmers. They *must* plant something else instead."

Carver was spending a great deal of time in his laboratory now. If the farmers were going to raise sweet potatoes, he must find ways of using them. There wasn't much of a market for sweet potatoes—they spoiled too easily.

So in his laboratory the professor dried sweet potatoes and ground them and made a coffee substitute out of them. He peeled and grated them and out of their milky juice made starch. He boiled the water that settled on top and made a syrup.

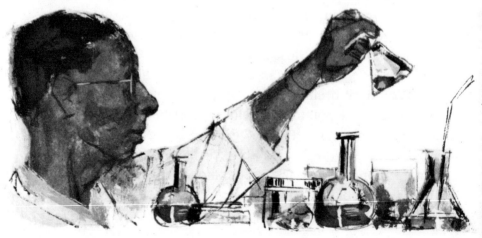

Then he went out and taught the farmers. "Lay the sweet potatoes out in the sun and dry them—or dry them on the back of your stoves." He showed the wives how to make sweet potato starch and coffee and syrup.

And he told the farmers about the boll weevil.

"That little black bug," he said, "is coming, and you had better get ready. If you go on planting only cotton, you will be in trouble deep. The boll weevil will eat you out of house and home. Nothing will stop that little bug. Plant enough sweet potatoes so you can sell some. Plant cowpeas. Plant peanuts. They will be your cash crop."

Peanuts? The farmers opened their eyes wide at that one. A few families grew a few peanut vines, but that was only on account of the children. The children loved goobers. But could goobers be a farm crop?

Carver had wondered about that himself once. Lately he had stopped wondering. He had come to believe that the answer he had so long looked for lay in sweet potatoes and peanuts—in those two together. Together they could be the lifesavers of the South. They could even lick the boll weevil.

267

Peanuts were not a new idea with him. He had started planting them 'way back in 1896. But that was because of the nitrogen they put back into the soil. At that time he hadn't known much about the nuts themselves. Since then he had taken the peanut into the laboratory and been amazed by what he found. The peanut was an almost magical food.

It was chock-full of nourishment. A pound of peanuts contained more protein than a pound of sirloin steak. It contained as much carbohydrates as a pound of potatoes. And on top of all that it had one-third as much fat as a pound of butter.

"Plant sweet potatoes, plant peanuts," Carver told the farmers.

He published a bulletin giving directions for growing peanuts. At the end he gave 105 peanut recipes.

One day he said to Washington: "Ask some of your friends to lunch. The Senior girls will cook it. Everything will be made of peanuts."

Ten people sat down at table. The girls served a five-course meal.

First came soup, then mock chicken with peanuts creamed as a vegetable and peanut bread. After that there was a salad. After the salad came ice cream and cookies. Last of all coffee

268

and candy were served. Everything was made from peanuts and nothing tasted the same. One guest after another declared, "I have never eaten a tastier or more satisfying lunch."

"Plant peanuts," Carver told the farmers.

Some of the Negro farmers listened. The peanut was a curious plant, but they had grown up with it and understood its ways. Even their ancestors in Africa had known the peanut. It had traveled from Peru to Spain, from Spain to Africa, from Africa back with the slaves. "Goober" was one of the few African words in the English language.

The Negro farmers listened. Peanuts were easy to raise. Peanuts didn't mind a drought. When there was no rain, they just curled up and waited for it. Then when rain came, the plants raced right ahead. The flowers matured and withered. The stems grew long and bent towards the ground. The pods dug themselves into the earth. In the earth, in the dark, they ripened like potatoes.

Some of the white farmers listened to Carver, too. The man who had raised nearly a bale and a quarter of cotton on an acre was worth listening to. Here and there acres of peanuts began to take the place of cotton.

Carver was sure he hadn't made a mistake about peanuts.

269

They were one of God's greatest gifts. People just didn't know it. They thought of peanuts as "monkey food"—something to take along when you went to the zoo. They thought peanuts were for circuses and carnivals, a treat for the children, that's all.

For such things there were enough peanuts being imported from abroad. What was to be done with the extra ones?

"I have to find ways of using peanuts so there will be a market for them," Carver decided.

And he shut himself up in his laboratory to try.

"Tell me, Great Creator, why did you make the peanut?"

Very often this thought passed through the professor's head. For he believed firmly that everything had been made for a purpose. Now he said the words aloud. And in the silence of the lonely room it seemed to him that he heard a voice answering.

"I have given you three laws—compatibility, temperature, and pressure. All you have to do is take the different parts of the peanut and put them together. Observe the laws. And I will show you why I made the peanut."

A hundred experiments flashed through the professor's mind. He would put the parts of the peanut together again—but in different ways. He would try combining this part with that under different conditions. He would use more heat or less, use more pressure or less.

In God's Little Workshop, George Carver kept on working with the peanut. He had not yet learned all the reasons why God had made it. But every day or two a new bottle or jar or box containing a new wonder joined the collection on the shelves.

Here were foods of all kinds—meal, instant coffee, chili sauce, mixed pickles, a dozen different drinks.

Here were salve, bleach, ink, rubbing oil, shampoo, shaving cream, axle grease, metal polish.

Here were linoleum, paper, plastics, wood filler, washing powder, synthetic rubber.

And here was peanut milk. Cream would rise upon it as on cow's milk. You could take the cream off and make it into butter. You could make it into cheese.

It takes courage to break the habit of years, and cotton was an old, old habit. But what with the boll weevil on the one hand and Professor Carver on the other, the peanut was taking hold. By 1919 it had really become a crop.

Who would ever have thought anyone would be grateful to the boll weevil? But there it was. In the public square of Enterprise, Alabama, a monument had been put up to the little black bug.

"In profound appreciation of the boll weevil and what it has done. As the herald of prosperity, this monument was erected by the citizens of Enterprise, Coffee County, Alabama." That's how the inscription read.

It was clear to everyone who saw the fine peanut shelling plant in Enterprise why the monument had been erected. In Coffee County the boll weevil had pushed King Cotton from his throne. King Peanut ruled instead. Every cotton farmer in the county had been so down and out in 1915 that nobody could pay his bills. After four years of raising peanuts, Coffee County was the most prosperous in Alabama.

Yes, peanuts were definitely moving up. They were a crop. In 1919, when Enterprise put up the monument, about half the peanuts consumed in the United States were grown at home. The peanut industry was worth 80 million dollars, and it was still an infant.

EVEN today when you build something that has never been built before, much of it must be done by hand. But at least you have good steel to work with and all kinds of machinery to help shape the various pieces. In forging the parts for his submarine, Robert Fulton had to depend almost entirely on blacksmiths. Blacksmiths are rare today, but if you have ever seen one, you know what a tedious job it is to shape an object with quick blows of a heavy hammer, then return the object to the forge to heat it red-hot again so that further shaping can be done.

Think of the weeks and months it took to build Robert Fulton's submarine—of the problems to be conquered, of the mistakes to be corrected. Compared with today's submarines his was a toy, with its hand cranks and propellers. But it was the forerunner of the powerful undersea ship of today, just as the Wright brothers' flimsy flying machine was the great-grandfather of all aircraft.

A Daring Voyage

BY
RALPH NADING HILL

Illustrated by
Howard Simon

From dawn until dark Robert haunted Périer's workshop in Rouen where his ship was being built. Gradually it took shape until, one day in 1800, its proud young builder could say that it was finished. The French government had given him no help but was glad to have an official committee on hand for the trial trip.

News reached many ears that the *Nautilus*—as Robert called his submarine—would be tested in July. Early in the morning of the day that the test took place a crowd had al-

272

ready gathered on the banks of the river Seine. The *Nautilus* was floating in the river, and Robert with two sailors was getting ready to submerge. At last the official inspection committee arrived with Mr. Forfait, the Minister of the Marine in Napoleon's cabinet.

"We shall now enter the *Nautilus*," Robert announced just before the trial trip, "dive to the bottom of the river, and remain submerged for forty-five minutes. This experiment will prove that in this ship it is possible to live for a long period under the sea. Here the shallowness of the river will not permit us to move about under water. However, we hope the value of an invisible ship that is at home under the waves will become clear to the most doubtful observer."

Scarcely a whisper could be heard in the crowd on the bank

as the two sailors climbed down into the *Nautilus,* followed by Robert, who shut the escape hatch after him. Proceeding slowly along the surface to deeper water, the strange craft stopped. Then, after a few moments, it began to sink. Soon nothing was visible except the bulge in the top where the hatch was located. Seconds later that, too, disappeared. The observers on the bank, craning their necks, could hardly believe what they were seeing.

"It is a foolish experiment," one of them said.

"They are trapped like rats!" muttered another.

As the minutes ticked by and there was not the slightest sign of motion near the spot where the *Nautilus* had gone down, hope for the occupants of the strange craft began to fade away. When forty-five endless minutes had passed and there was still no sign of the submarine, the official inspectors looked at one another gravely, shrugged their shoulders and whispered in low tones. The crowd was silent.

Presently, near the spot where the *Nautilus* had gone down, bubbles could be seen. In a few seconds a gray form appeared. A shout went up from the bank. Within minutes the *Nautilus* was in full view again. Suddenly the door on the top opened and the tall, lithe figure of Robert Fulton appeared! Cheers now rang out from the bank. The government inspectors were talking excitedly among themselves. One had to see such an exhibition to believe it. Unquestionably the submarine would become a great weapon of the sea.

All eyes were fastened on the inventor and the two members of his crew as they approached the bank. Robert's face, lighted with smiles, was a study in modesty mixed with pride.

"Monsieur," announced the Minister of the Marine, Mr. Forfait, "I have no doubt of the value of your machine. This has been a great spectacle!"

274

Robert went home that night as tired and as happy as the victor in an athletic contest. The Minister of the Marine had promised to send Napoleon a most enthusiastic report of the *Nautilus*. Through Mr. Forfait it seemed certain that a loan of 6,000 francs would be obtained from the French government to pay for further experiments. Although this was but a fraction of the 28,000 francs of his own money that Robert had had to spend, it was better than nothing. And probably more money would be coming from the government later.

But his hopes were to be dashed again. Weeks passed and the government did nothing. All Robert was able to get from Napoleon was a statement in writing that if he were captured by the British during his experiments at sea, he would be treated like any French sailor who had fallen into the hands of the enemy. If the British did not treat him in such a manner, then the French government would take revenge upon British captives held in France.

Spending his own money, Robert now decided to try out his submarine in the English Channel. The craft was towed down the River Seine to the seaport of Le Havre, where the inventor was able to practice in deep water off the shore. Making repeated dives, Fulton and his two sailors tested the hand cranks connected to the propellers and perfected the torpedoes. It was at this point that he decided upon a three-man attack against the British Navy, which today seems absurd. Through the French Intelligence, he planned to find out where the English ships were anchored. Then he and his crew would set out one day across the English Channel to reach them, traveling much of the way on the surface.

Outside the harbor where the English ships were anchored, the submarine would dive and steal shoreward until it was beside a British man-of-war. There Fulton would affix his torpedo to the hull of the enemy ship, turn about and make all possible headway toward the open sea. As he withdrew, an explosion

would rock the water, and there would be one less British frigate strangling the freedom of the seas. To our ears this scheme sounds as foolhardy as sailing over an enemy anti-air-craft battery in a gas balloon, but Robert none the less embarked upon it.

On September 12, 1800, he and his crew of two sailors set out from France into the English Channel. Rocking along the surface with the aid of a sail affixed to the top of the submarine, the three adventurers at first met good weather. Their destination, a point a little over seven miles from the Marcou Islands, might have been reached in fairly good time except for a series of storms. Wild enough on fair days, the Channel writhed with jagged waves, battering the *Nautilus* about like a barrel. When the skies cleared and the submarine proved to

be still watertight, it proceeded on its course. At last it reache_
its destination, a small harbor where British ships were known
to ride at anchor.

Robert chose midnight as the hour for his attack. In a calm
sea he furled his sail, descended into the dank interior of the
ship, closed the hatch after him and opened a valve. A rush of
water filled the ballast tanks, and the *Nautilus* began to sink.
Down the three men went, crowded together in the tiny chamber, a flickering candle casting strange shadows on its sweat-
ing iron walls. At once the sailors began to turn the hand
cranks as Robert guided their course with his compass and
barometer. The *Nautilus* labored forward.

"Faster, boys!" urged Robert, breaking a long silence. "We
will never make it if the tide turns before we reach the harbor!"
The sailors redoubled their efforts, their legs cramped and ach-
ing, their arms taut and strained as they tugged at the clumsy
cranks. For a few minutes the *Nautilus* moved briskly forward,
but then she began to slow down despite the mighty efforts of
the two sailors at their cranks. Now the ship was almost at a
standstill.

"We are too late," said Fulton in despair. "The tide has
turned!" Breathing heavily the crewmen relaxed at their
cranks. Robert pumped water out of the ballast tanks and
turned the propeller on top of the vessel. The *Nautilus* began
to rise until she was just below the surface. The pipes to admit
air to the compartment were thrust up, and the candle was
blown out to conserve oxygen. Finally the anchor was dropped.

"We are so close to our target," announced Fulton, "that
they would spot us if we were to surface. We must remain submerged until the next tide."

Silence now filled the damp compartment, only four feet
high, as the men stretched their legs as best they could and
278

prepared to sit out the opposing tide, which would run for six hours. Little was said. With nothing to do, the two sailors' imaginations ran to thoughts of death by drowning or possibly by explosion. Suppose the British should see their air pipe at dawn! Never should they have embarked on this crazy voyage! Now it was too late, and their only choice was to see it through.

As for Robert, he was thinking only of the task ahead. No possibility other than success even suggested itself. Daylight would come with the next tide; but if they remained submerged, there would be little chance of being discovered.

The six endless hours passed. When the *Nautilus* swung about on its anchor chain, Robert realized that the tide had turned. Hurriedly the ventilators were drawn down, the anchor hauled in and the ballast tanks filled. As the vessel began to sink, the sailors returned to their cranks and Robert to his instruments. At length the *Nautilus* found its way into the harbor toward its objective. The torpedoes were placed in readiness. The crucial moment had come!

But had it? In the next few moments Fulton realized his bitter bad luck. In the interval between the tides the two British ships had hoisted sail and departed. At first he could not bring himself to believe this, but when the *Nautilus* cautiously surfaced and he could view the full sweep of the harbor, there was no doubt that they were gone. "Fulton luck!" he moaned as he climbed wearily back into the compartment. Now the *Nautilus* turned about for the long journey back to France, which it reached without further trouble.

That fall he sailed on another expedition against the same two ships, but they eluded him once more. He found that the watchful British Intelligence had learned of his plans and had warned the commanders of the brigs. Now it was turning cold, and he had to put the *Nautilus* up for the winter. Nevertheless he persisted in his campaign to interest the French government, which finally granted him 10,000 francs for further experiments. A liberal prize in money was added for any ship he managed to sink. This was encouraging as he had already spent much more than three times this amount of his own money.

During the following year he worked hard on new ideas for a larger submarine that would stay under water for eight hours, and on better methods of releasing his torpedoes. All this effort was costing him more money. Meanwhile the French government was still sitting on the fence waiting to see how he came out before granting him any large sum. Faced with such apathy, he could not continue forever as a combination inventor, financier and undersea navy. Even if it was not his nature to give up, he still had to yield to such odds. Perhaps he was a "visionary." Perhaps his submarine was, after all, just a "mad scheme."

Some men succeed very young in this world. Others are old by the time they achieve their aims. And of course a great many, perhaps the majority, never really succeed at all. In 1801 Robert had reached the age of thirty-six. He was not old, but his youth was certainly behind him. He had failed as an artist, and he had not truly succeeded as an inventor. But defeat sometimes serves merely to spur the defeated on to greater efforts. So it was with Robert Fulton, who had rare spirit. Each defeat had left him abler and stronger.

TORRENCE Huffman, President of the Dayton Bank, owned an eighty-acre cow pasture outside the town. Will and Orv asked him if they could use the cow pasture.

"Somebody told me you two have been experimenting with flying machines." Mr. Huffman smiled. "Is that right?"

"That's right," Wilbur said.

"Go ahead, boys, use the field," Mr. Huffman said, "but don't kill any of my cows."

The brothers had decided to build a new flying machine with a sixteen horsepower engine. They worked very hard at it and now, embittered by the attitude of their neighbors, they seldom saw anyone but Charley Taylor and their sister Kate. When they walked along the street, people winked at each other as if to say, "They're the ones who said they flew." Will and Orv ignored the winks and the scorn, but it hurt them to know that their own neighbors thought they had lied.

Airplane in a Cow Pasture

BY QUENTIN REYNOLDS

Illustrated by Jacob Landau

Mr. Chanute knew they hadn't lied. He went to Paris and made a speech about the flight at Kitty Hawk, and everyone in France became excited about the flying machine the Wright brothers had built. They were famous in France, and then in Germany and England, but not in Dayton.

"Why don't they stick to their bicycle shop?" the people said, but the two brothers went right on working. They brought their new flying machine to the cow pasture. But they

281

tried it out only early in the morning. Nobody was going to have a chance to laugh at them. Their new flying machine stayed up longer than the Kitty Hawk machine.

Then one day Wilbur actually circled the field. The new flying machine could steer. Miracles were happening at this cow pasture every day, but no one saw them except a few cows down at the far end of the pasture. A few days later Orv circled the field three times—a distance of three miles.

One day Will and Orv asked their father and Kate to go to the cow pasture with them.

"Be sure and bring your watch, Father," Will said.

Kate and Bishop Wright stood beside the flying machine.

"I want you to time this flight," Wilbur said. "I've filled the gasoline tank. Now, Orv, take her up."

Orv took her up. The flying machine almost disappeared in the distance, and then it turned and came back. Orv flew over

his father's head and waved to him. Then he made a large circle around the field. Bishop Wright kept one eye on his watch. The minutes passed. Fifteen . . . twenty . . . thirty.

"He's been up there half an hour, Will!" Bishop Wright said excitedly.

Finally the flying machine swooped to a gentle landing.

"Thirty-nine minutes!" Bishop Wright gasped.

"I only came down because I ran out of gasoline," Orv explained.

"We can stay up almost as long as we want," Wilbur said. "But we wanted you to see our airplane actually in action."

"Airplane? That's a good name for it," the Bishop said.

Bishop Wright told a few people what he had seen at the cow pasture. They believed him, and now they were willing to believe Wilbur and Orville. People hurried to the bicycle shop to congratulate them, but the two brothers were too busy to see them.

"Where were they when we came back from Kitty Hawk?" Will asked bitterly.

"Well, we've gotten along without them all these years," Orv said. "We can still get along without them."

One day two important men arrived in Dayton. One was French; the other was English. Each wanted to buy the Wright brothers' airplane. Each wanted to pay a huge sum for the exclusive rights to it so that only his country could make it.

"The Germans will make war on us one day," the Frenchman said excitedly, "and with this flying machine we can beat them easily. We can fly over their armies and drop dynamite on them."

"We too fear Germany," the Englishman said, "and we are willing to pay you anything you want for the right to make your airplane."

"But we are Americans," Wilbur said. "If we gave the airplane to anyone it would be to our own army."

"But Monsieur Wright, if you will forgive me," the Frenchman said, "your own army has already refused it. Your own army is not interested."

Wilbur was startled. It is true that he and Orv had written to the army authorities in Washington, and that the army hadn't been interested. But neither he nor Orv had told anybody about this.

"Nevertheless," Wilbur said now, "we are Americans, and some day perhaps our army will be interested."

The two polite gentlemen from abroad bowed, looked regretful, and left.

"I guess we'd better give a real demonstration," Will said. "I don't blame our army authorities for not being enthusiastic. They've never seen our plane fly."

"All right, Will, we'll give them something to think about," Orv said.

Theodore Roosevelt was President of the United States then. Although he is remembered as a man of action, he was a great reader, and one day he picked up a copy of the *Scientific American*. There was an article in it about the Wright brothers and their flying machine.

"Get hold of these two young men," President Roosevelt told his Secretary of War, "and have them give an exhibition. Maybe they have something in that flying machine."

One day a dignified colonel arrived in Dayton. He went to see the Wright brothers. Would they be so good as to honor a request by the President of the United States?

"Frankly, gentlemen," the colonel said, "we in the army don't think the flying machine has any future, but the President has ordered us to get in touch with you. Will you give a demonstration of your machine?"

284

"You bet we will," Orville replied, and Wilbur nodded vigorously.

"Of course we will see that it is held in secret," the colonel said, smiling.

"Why?" Wilbur asked.

"Well, in case things go wrong . . . I mean if it doesn't get off the ground . . ." The colonel faltered. "We don't want you gentlemen to be humiliated."

"Don't worry about us, Colonel," and Orv laughed. "Ask a thousand, ask a million people to the demonstration. We don't care."

A huge crowd assembled at Fort Myer, Virginia, the place the army had picked out for the test. The Secretary of War was there. A dozen generals were present and at least fifty reporters. Nobody really believed that the queer-looking machine could actually fly. Did it fly? Orville took it up and circled the field for one hour. When he landed the crowd went wild with enthusiasm. Even generals with three stars on their shoulders swarmed all over the two calm, unexcited brothers.

"I'd give anything to ride with you in that new flying

machine," a young lieutenant said. Orville looked at him. The young soldier's eyes were shining. He was Lieutenant Fred Lahm.

"Well, come on, Lieutenant," Orville said. "Climb up in back of me and hang on. . . . Clear the crowd away, please."

The crowd fell back. Orv took off easily with the lieutenant hanging on. They circled the field three times and then landed. The crowd was almost hysterical. It had seen a miracle happen. The generals were thoughtful. This airplane could carry a 180-pound passenger in addition to its pilot. That meant it could carry a 180-pound bomb. Perhaps it could carry more than one bomb.

"Have you sold the rights to this plane to any foreign government?" a general asked.

"We're Americans, General," Orv said simply.

The general shook his hand and said, "Will you have time to see the Secretary of War tomorrow?" The two brothers nodded.

The next morning they woke up to find themselves famous. Every newspaper in the country had headlines about their flight. They were the most famous men in the world now. There were big crowds outside the War Department building when they went to see the Secretary of War.

"You've done a great thing, young men," the Secretary of War said, shaking hands with them. "The first men in history to fly. Tell me, can you build larger airplanes than the one you showed us yesterday?"

"It's just a matter of power," Orville said. "If we make stronger, more powerful engines, we can fly bigger airplanes."

"If the power is there we can make a kitchen table fly," Wilbur said.

"I'm sure you can," the Secretary said. "We want you to build airplanes for our army. Will you?"

286

"Of course we will," Orv said, and Wilbur added, a bit embarrassed, "I hate to mention it, Mr. Secretary, but . . . we have no money. We spent our last cent to finish the plane we showed you yesterday."

"You'll never need money again." The Secretary smiled. "We'll advance all the money you need. Can you build an airplane that will go forty miles an hour?"

"You name the speed you want," Orv said. "We'll build it to your specifications."

"May we make them in Dayton?" Will said. "That's our home town."

"Of course you may," the Secretary of War said. "When are you planning to return?"

"On the midnight train," Will told him.

"That'll give you time to accept a dinner invitation," the Secretary said, smiling. "The President of the United States has asked me to extend an invitation to dinner tonight. Can you make it?"

Wilbur looked at Orville. Orville looked at Wilbur.

Orville winked at Wilbur. "I think we can make it," he said gravely.

And then the two boys who had learned to fly walked out of the office, arm in arm.

MOST of us think of broadcasting as sending programs out into the air for millions of people to enjoy. That is an important part of broadcasting because it provides entertainment. People always need some entertainment to go along with their work.

But there is another kind of broadcasting which, in some ways, is even more important than entertainment. This is the broadcasting that goes on every day and every night but which most people never see or hear. Some of this is radio; some of this is television.

Often it is easy to forget the real magic—and usefulness—of radio. It is not only that voices can be sent back and forth through the air but that this can be done while both the transmitter and the receiver are moving.

"Calling All Cars"

BY JACK GOULD

Illustrated by Bette J. Davis

You are familiar with a moving receiver because this is what you have when you turn on a radio in a car. As you go speeding along the road, you can listen to music or news reports.

It is just as easy to put a transmitter in a car. You can use the same aerial—the long rod that goes up above the top of the car and looks like a fishing pole. All you need is a button. When you push the button, you can transmit and talk to another car or a central headquarters. Release the button, and you are ready to hear someone speak to you.

When we put a receiver and a transmitter together like this, we have a *radiotelephone*. We can install radiotelephones in cars, ships, airplanes, railroad trains, buses, trucks and taxicabs. Even if you are riding on a lonely road, or high in

the sky over a range of mountains, or out in the middle of the ocean, you can always be in touch with the world!

There are even portable television stations that can be put in an automobile. The camera is put on top of the car and the transmitter equipment in the back seat. The pictures are sent through the tiny stations, which then shoot the waves directly up to a big receiving tower. Without being near the car, we can see where it is going.

The list of special things that radio and television can do is a long and interesting one. In going down the list, you will be able to see for yourself why broadcasting can be so fascinating.

Police departments all over the country have used radio for many years because it is often the quickest way to catch criminals.

Suppose someone telephones the police to say that his house is being robbed. This is what happens:

The sergeant answering the telephone in the police station asks for the address of the house where the robbery is taking place. He passes the information on to the radio dispatcher, who knows where the radio patrol cars are cruising around the city.

He notifies the cars nearest to the robbery like this: "Calling Cars 12 and 14!"

The dispatcher tells the policemen in the cars the address of the crime and then adds "Signal 35." The policemen know that "Signal 35" means a robbery. Other signals may mean a man has a gun, or there is an automobile accident, or someone is just disturbing the peace of the community. Different police departments have different signals.

In a matter of minutes after receiving the alarm, the radio patrol cars are at the scene of the crime. Often they catch a robber before he even has a chance to get out of a house. In the days before radio, the police would have to send a car all the way from headquarters, which might have been many miles away. Often they arrived too late.

When somebody is hurt in an accident or is suddenly taken sick, the first person you want is the doctor. But often the doctor may be on his way from one patient's home to another patient's home. It is then that the radiotelephone is used to advise the doctor of an emergency.

291

But there is also another system: the *radio message center.* With this system, the doctor needs only a receiver. When somebody wants to reach the doctor, he calls the message center. From the center the doctor's number is broadcast over and over again. When the doctor hears it, he goes to a telephone and calls the center which gives him the message.

The newest railroad trains use radio in many different ways. In the club car, where passengers can smoke or order refreshments, there is a radiotelephone in a booth, just like the telephone booth in a drugstore. All the passenger does is lift the receiver in the booth and ask for the operator. Then the passenger can call any number in the country.

Another use for radio is on freight trains. The engineer in the locomotive has a radiotelephone which he uses to call the brakeman in the caboose.

If a freight train has a hundred cars, you can see how much easier it is to use radio than to walk on top of the cars all the way up to the engineer. Or if the engineer wants, he can talk to the engineer of a train coming in the opposite direction.

Big ocean-going ships have many kinds of radio, too. One radio is tuned always to what is known as *the international distress frequency.* This is the frequency which can be used by a ship only when it is in danger of sinking or needs help immediately. It is the S O S frequency.

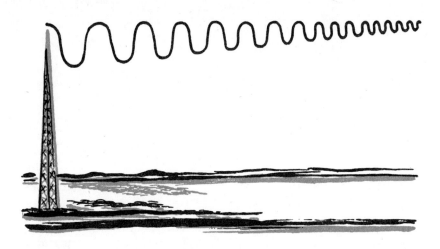

Ships also have radiotelephones for the passengers, called *ship-to-shore* telephones. Then, there are short wave radios to pick up the news and weather reports.

Airplanes depend on radio for their take-off, their flight and their landing. The pilot has several different radiotelephones in a big plane because sometimes he must use different wave lengths, depending on whether he wants to send a message over a long distance or a short distance.

When a plane goes out on the runway, the control tower at the airport uses radio to tell the pilot when he is to take off. Once the plane is in the air, the pilot is told at what altitude he must fly. Except in an emergency, when he does whatever he thinks best, a pilot cannot change his altitude without obtaining permission from the nearest control tower.

There is another protection for airplanes flying through the air. It is called *riding the beam*. The *beam* is really just a continuous series of radio signals sent out in one direction in the same way that a flashlight will send out a beam of light.

As long as the pilot hears the signals, he knows he is "on the beam" and will be guided straight to his destination.

At the landing field, another control tower uses radio to tell the pilot if it is his turn to land, or whether he must circle around overhead—the pilots call this being "stacked up"—until the runways are clear.

The *walkie-talkie* used by soldiers is really just a small radiotelephone. It is intended for use only over short distances, a few miles at most, so not very many tubes are needed and the equipment is light enough for one man to carry. Walkie-talkies are often used by firemen at big fires. Often it is important for a fireman to be able to call the fire truck and order more hose or equipment.

Television still is so new that scientists constantly are discovering new ways to use the camera. Recently, the English Navy found it helpful in locating a submarine that had sunk. They put a television camera in a watertight container and then dropped it over the side of a rescue ship. When they turned the camera on, they were able to see the submarine in deep water.

Perhaps some day television can be used to find the wrecks of ancient pirate ships or to explore other mysteries at the bottom of the sea.

EVER since the beginning of time, man always has wished that he could see in darkness. Now he can, through an invention that already has changed the course of history. It is the invention of *radar*.

The word radar stands for *Radio Detection and Ranging*. "Detection" means to find out where something is, and "Ranging" means to find out how far away that something is and, if it is moving, where it is going.

That is what radar does. It uses waves to go out into space and bring back a picture of what lies farther away than the eye can see. Darkness, fog, storm and smoke screens do not affect these waves. The electronic "eyes" of radar are ready always to warn us of trouble ahead.

It was radar that helped save England from the German airplanes during World War II. The Nazis sent swarms of planes over London in what is called "The Battle of Britain." They hoped to

Round-Trip to the Moon

BY JACK GOULD

Illustrated by Bette J. Davis

crush the capital of the British Empire, which was then fighting almost alone, and to end the war quickly. England had only a few airplanes but very brave pilots.

With the help of radar, English airmen knew when Nazi planes were coming long before they reached London. With their few airplanes, they took off quickly and were in the sky when the Nazis arrived. Instead of finding London a defenseless city, the Nazis found the British ready for dogfights. After several raids, the Germans lost so many airplanes that the Nazi air force was never the same again. It was one of the turning points of the war.

Radar works like a rubber ball thrown against a stone wall.

If we throw a ball fast enough against a wall, we know that it will come right back to us.

Now imagine that we knew how fast we threw the ball. Suppose we say that in one second the ball traveled ten feet.

Let's throw the ball against the wall a second time and have a friend hold a watch and tell us how long it takes the ball to make the round-trip from your hand to the wall and back again to your hand.

Our friend looks at his watch and says the round-trip took exactly two seconds.

10 feet in one second

10 feet in one second

We know that in each second the ball can travel ten feet.

Since it took two seconds for the round-trip, that means the ball traveled a total of twenty feet.

But we only want to know how far away the wall is from your hand. So we divide the round-trip in half. Half of twenty is ten. So the distance from the hand to the wall is ten feet.

In radar, it is the wave that takes the place of the rubber ball. At a radar station, a transmitter and a receiver are put side by side.

First, a signal—called a *pulse*—makes a wave that is sent out into the air from the transmitter. Then the transmitter is shut off, and the receiver is turned on. The signal goes out

296

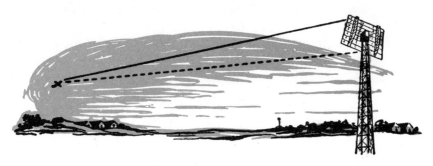

until it "hits" something like the stone wall—maybe it is a ship or maybe it is a plane. Then the signal bounces off the ship or the plane and comes back to the receiver. When it gets to the receiver the signal goes to a picture tube and makes a tiny flicker of light.

We know a radio signal always travels at the same speed—186,000 miles a second. And we easily can tell how long the signal traveled. We measure the time between when it left the transmitter and when it came back to the receiver. So now we can tell how far the signal traveled. Just as we did with the rubber ball, we then divide that distance in half and we know how far away the plane is.

With a real radar set all the calculations are done automatically. All the radar operator does is look at the picture tube, and he gets his answer right away.

Because radio signals travel so much faster than the airplane, radar can follow the plane right across the sky. The face of the radar screen is divided into little squares. Then, on the screen, it shows where the plane is going to be in a couple of seconds. If the plane is first spotted at A, we know it will soon be at B.

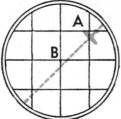

This is time enough to aim and fire a shell from a gun if the plane is sent over by an enemy. The shell arrives at B just at the same moment as the plane. Down goes the plane in an explosion!

Another kind of radar sends out and receives a lot of waves. When enough waves are bounced back, it gives us a whole picture of what they have "hit."

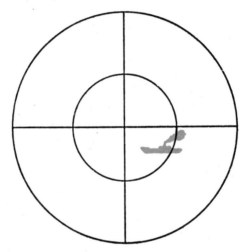

You can see how important radar is to ships and airplanes that must go through darkness, storms and fogs. One ship can tell if another ship is crossing its path, or if there is an iceberg ahead. Radar is so sensitive that it can even pick out the conning tower of an enemy submarine.

With radar, an airplane can tell if there is a mountain ahead, or if it is flying too close to the ground. Small radar sets are put in bombers and jet planes. With radar, although the bombardier often cannot see the target with his eye, he can put the bomb right where he wants it.

But the most dramatic story of radar took place on a lonely hill in New Jersey on a cold night in January, 1946. On the

298

hill was a plain wooden building surrounded by high fences. Soldiers were on guard.

On top of the building was a strange rectangular piece of metal. It looked like a big bedspring, and it was pointed up to the heavens. It was a special radar aerial.

Inside the building, there were Army officers huddled over mysterious looking radar sets. Everyone was very still. Hour after hour they waited. An officer finally looked at his watch. "All right," he said.

Suddenly there was heard in the room a signal that sounded like this:

BEEP

Everyone held his breath and counted to himself: *One Two—*

They waited a fraction of a second more. Then they heard the sound that was to make history:

BEEP

For the first time, man had shown that he could "communicate" with the moon!

The big BEEP was a radar signal sent up to the face of the moon. The little BEEP was all the strength that the signal had left, after it had come back to earth.

Scientists now know they can use the moon like the backboard of a basketball court. They can send signals up to the moon at an angle and have them come back to earth hundreds and hundreds of miles away.

If scientists can find ways to send steadier and stronger signals thousands and thousands of miles up into the sky, they will have one of the secrets for guiding space and rocket ships into places that no man has ever seen.

Perhaps some day there will be a television camera in the nose of a space ship. Then millions of people can see what lies in outer space.

If this seems like a dream, you should remember something. Only sixty years ago—less than the average lifetime of one person—radio and television were only dreams.

DID you ever hear of Hero of Alexandria? Nobody seems to know just when he lived, but it was about 100 B.C. Even at this early date he was working with siphons and coin-in-the-slot machines, and even with the idea of jet propulsion. His most famous gadget was a little engine that was turned by steam issuing from jets equally spaced around the boiler. The same principle has been put to work in our modern steam turbines and, more recently, in gas turbines which operate in jet-propelled airplanes.

Remember the last time you stepped from a canoe to a dock? Do you remember how careful you had to be? You found, didn't you, that the canoe had a tendency to move back just as you stepped forward. If you were silly enough to try to jump for the dock you may not have made it at all. Hero of Alexandria invented a little engine that ran by using this same idea of a force pushing backward. You can build yourself

Jet Propulsion

BY NELSON F. BEELER
AND
FRANKLYN M. BRANLEY

Illustrated by Serge Hollerbach

a little "interaction" motor and see how this backward push can be turned into round-and-round motion.

Get a tin can which has had the top cut off smoothly. With an ice-pick or sharp nail, punch a series of about 16 evenly spaced holes near the bottom. Pry the tool to the right each time so that every hole faces that direction.

Punch two holes near the top of the can and opposite each other. Put a four-foot length of thread or light string through each of these holes, and join them about ten inches above the mouth of the can.

301

Now take up your engine by the ends of the threads and hold it under the tap in the bathtub. Turn on the faucet, regulating the flow of water until as much enters the can at the top as leaves through the holes at the bottom. The can will start spinning rapidly.

Each bit of water leaving a hole pushes back on the can. This action going on at all the jets at the same time creates a "torque" or twist. In Hero's engine, each jet of steam produced an interaction and so it rotated this same way.

In the jet-propelled airplane, gases are compressed and exploded in the engine and allowed to leave at the back, expanding as they go. Each molecule of gas as it leaves pushes against the airplane, driving it forward. The jet-propelled engine has to suck in air through the front in order to get oxygen for combustion, but it can run on cheap fuel like kerosene and is surprisingly efficient. Rockets are driven forward the same way, but they carry their own fuel and oxygen so that they can work in a vacuum; in fact, they are more efficient there.

As you read further in science you will get used to seeing this old elementary principle applied over and over again in newer devices. In science there is actually "nothing new under the sun!"

CHEMISTRY is Nature's magic. The more we learn about it the more it seems as though some great invisible magician were behind the scenes performing one miracle after another.

Chemistry is working on everyone in the world every second of the day and night. It is working on you right now, keeping you strong and healthy so that you can play on the school team or swim or race or do anything else you want to do. Think of that cereal that you ate for breakfast this morning or those glasses of milk you drink every day. Slowly and constantly they are being changed into new muscle and stronger bones and teeth and hair and skin. Now you begin to see how wonderful chemistry is.

Chemistry Is Nature's Magic

BY JEROME S. MEYER

Illustrated by Charles Clement

Chemistry is really the fascinating story of the HOW and the WHY of everything we see around us. It enables us to know just what things are made of and why they differ from each other. It tells us how to transfer one thing into another and how to get exactly the substance we want merely by adding a little of this to a little of that.

Nearly everything we use, nearly every invention made for our comfort comes from a knowledge of chemistry. This book and all other books, as well as all magazines and newspapers, would be impossible without chemistry. The paper in a book, the type and ink that print it, all the pictures in it and even the glue that holds the pages together, are all chemical processes. The same is true for all the pictures you see in newspapers and

303

magazines, because photography is mostly chemical and without chemistry there could be no pictures of any kind—not even the movies!

Chemistry tells the farmer what to add to the soil to get the best crops and produce the best foods. It tells the engineer how to purify the rain water and make it fit for all of us to drink. It tells the doctor what medicine or tonics to give us to make us well when we are sick. It supplies our drug stores with thousands of different medicines and tonics and lotions and pills to keep us well and strong. It has given us such valuable things as soap, cellophane, paint, ink, glass, and plastics of all kinds that make dolls, boats, and hundreds of other toys. It has also given us thousands of other useful articles, like fountain pens, toothbrushes, telephones, electric equipment, and so many other things that it would take up ten more pages to list them.

And how would you like to live in an igloo or a house made of mud? You would have to if it were not for chemistry, because bricks, cement, mortar, steel, and even lumber are all made possible through our knowledge of chemistry. Chemistry gives us steel from the rough iron ore, and just think of the thousands of things made out of steel—the machines and the tools and the big locomotives and the huge skyscrapers and all the knives and nails and nuts and bolts and screws. If you think of all these, you will see how very valuable steel is to us and how important chemistry is, enabling us to fashion so many things from the rough iron ore that we dig right out of the ground.

Wherever we go, chemistry is with us. Outdoors the trees and flowers and bushes and fruits and vegetables that grow in our garden are constantly changing into all sorts of wonderful things that are good to eat or good to look at—all because of

304

the sunlight and soil and rain and gases in the air. And we, ourselves, are like small chemical laboratories. Every time we breathe we take oxygen right out of the air and turn it into another and entirely different gas when we exhale. Everything we eat and drink is digested by chemical processes and distributed to parts of our body or expelled as waste matter.

Now perhaps you can see that if it were not for our knowledge of chemistry we might all be living like the savages in the jungles of Siam or New Guinea. Then you can realize how important it is to know something about chemistry.

305

HOBBIES sometimes lead to discoveries. Take, for example, the hobby of Leeuwenhoek (lay'-ven-hook), who lived in Holland about 300 years ago. His hobby was grinding and polishing small pieces of glass. He worked on these pieces until he had shaped them into powerful magnifying glasses. (Special glasses like these, and others found in eyeglasses, telescopes, and cameras, are called lenses.)

So carefully did he do his work, that his magnifying lenses were stronger and clearer than any that had been made before. Leeuwenhoek looked at everything he could get hold of with his new lenses—the stinger of a bee, the tail of a fish, the leaf of a plant, a drop of milk, and many other things. One day he placed a little drop of pond water under his magnifying glass. To his great surprise, he found that this drop was filled with thousands of tiny plants and animals. He had discovered a new world of living things which had never been seen before.

To See the Very Small

BY JULIUS SCHWARTZ

Illustrated by Gil Miret

What makes a magnifying lens magnify? Is it because it is made of a special kind of glass? Or is there another reason? You can find out by making a lens yourself.

You will need: a piece of newspaper, a glass of water, a toothpick or a broomstraw, a saucer and a bit of kitchen fat.

In this experiment you are *not* going to use glass to make your lens. Instead you are going to use something which allows light to pass through it and can easily be shaped to make a lens. Can you guess what it is? Ordinary water!

Make a thin smear of fat on the newspaper to cover a space about the size of a penny. Be sure that a letter "o" is covered by the fat. Now dip the toothpick into the glass of water. Let a drop run off the toothpick onto a letter "o" of the print. Notice that the water does not soak into the paper, because the water and fat do not mix. Notice also that the water has formed a little round drop. Now look through this drop at the letter "o". Does this "o" look bigger than an "o" which is not under water? You have made a magnifying lens out of water!

Is it the water itself that does the magnifying, or is it something about the shape of the water drop? You can find the answer by tearing out the piece of greased newspaper and putting it in the center of the saucer. Now pour enough water from the glass into the saucer to cover the paper with a layer of water about ⅛ inch high. Now look at the print. Does it look any bigger than the print on a piece of dry newspaper?

When the water was in the shape of a curved drop, it made the print look bigger. When the water was in a flat layer, the print remained the same size.

It's all in the curve! And what is true for your water lens is also true for glass lenses.

Lenses have many uses. Teams of lenses working together in powerful microscopes help us see tiny objects that our eyes alone could not see—things like bacteria and the red cells in blood. Lenses in telescopes make faraway stars appear closer to us. Lenses in cameras help make pictures on the film. Lenses in eyeglasses make the world clearer for millions of people.

P. S.

 ${\rm I}$N preparing this volume, the editors have selected stories and excerpts from complete books, and in those cases where the text of a book is reprinted in its entirety, only a few of the many delightful illustrations from the original have been used. For the benefit of those who would like to read and enjoy the complete books, the following list is given.

All About Dinosaurs BY ROY CHAPMAN ANDREWS—Introducing Dinosaurs, 123
All About Radio and Television BY JACK GOULD—"Calling All Cars," 289; Round-Trip to the Moon, 295
All About the Stars BY ANNE TERRY WHITE—Portrait of the Sun, 37
All About the Weather BY IVAN RAY TANNEHILL—How We Measure and Observe the Weather, 59
All About Whales BY ROY CHAPMAN ANDREWS—The Land Animal That Went to Sea, 146
Asbestos BY LILIAN HOLMES STRACK—A Magic Mineral, 207
Ben Franklin of Old Philadelphia BY MARGARET COUSINS—Ben Franklin of Old Philadelphia, 234
Branches Green BY RACHEL FIELD—Something Told the Wild Geese, 86
The Bright Design BY KATHERINE B. SHIPPEN—The Scientists and the Bright Design, 170
Cautionary Verses BY HILAIRE BELLOC—The Vulture, 156
Couriers of the Sky BY MARY GRAHAM BONNER—Couriers of the Sky, 94
Experiments in Science BY NELSON F. BEELER AND FRANKLYN M. BRANLEY—Jet Propulsion, 301
Famous Bridges of the World BY DAVID B. STEINMAN—Bridges Help Us Every Day, 197
The First Book of Printing BY SAM AND BERYL EPSTEIN—Johann Gutenberg and His Type, 244
The First Great Inventions BY LANCELOT HOGBEN—A Hundred Years of Inventions, 175
Gaily the Troubadour BY ARTHUR GUITERMAN—Habits of the Hippopotamus, 157
The Garden of the World BY JANET MCGILL—Man-Made Plants, 191
George Washington Carver BY ANNE TERRY WHITE—Plant Peanuts, 263
The Grasshopper Book BY WILFRID S. BRONSON—Insect Music, 102
How the Earth Is Changing BY RUDOLPH BRETZ—The Ocean and Its Work, 10
How the World Grew Up BY GRACE KINER—The First Metal Workers, 186
Insects and Their Homes BY DOROTHY STERLING—They Build with Wax, 108
It's Fun to Know Why BY JULIUS SCHWARTZ—To See the Very Small, 306
John James Audubon BY MARGARET AND JOHN KIERAN—John James Audubon, 247
John Muir: Father of Our National Parks BY CHARLES NORMAN—John Muir Comes to America, 255

The Land We Live On BY CARROLL LANE FENTON AND MILDRED ADAMS FENTON—Across Our Country, 3

Lions, Gorillas and Their Neighbors BY CARL AND MARY L. J. AKELEY—Lion Adventures, 128

Mr. Bell Invents the Telephone BY KATHERINE B. SHIPPEN—Mr. Bell Invents the Telephone, 237

Peacock Pie BY WALTER DE LA MARE—Silver, 44

A Picture Book of Astronomy BY JEROME S. MEYER—The Stars, 30

A Picture Book of Chemistry BY JEROME S. MEYER—Chemistry Is Nature's Magic, 303

A Picture Book of Molecules and Atoms BY JEROME S. MEYER—Atoms Are Like Letters, 220

Play with Trees BY MILLICENT E. SELSAM—How to Know the Trees, 74

Poems for Youth BY EMILY DICKINSON—A Bird, 93

Radium BY LILIAN HOLMES STRACK—The Rock That Glowed in the Dark, 214

Robert Fulton and the Steamboat BY RALPH NADING HILL—A Daring Voyage, 272

The Second Jungle Book BY RUDYARD KIPLING—The Law of the Jungle, 159

The Sky Is Blue BY W. MAXWELL REED—Volcanoes and Earthquakes, 18

Slow Smoke BY LEW SARETT—Four Little Foxes, 122

Snakes BY HERBERT S. ZIM—Snakes, 120

The Story of Our Calendar BY RUTH BRINDZE—Counting Moons, 180

Thomas Alva Edison BY G. GLENWOOD CLARK—New Light for the World, 225

Wildlife for America BY EDWARD H. GRAHAM AND WILLIAM R. VAN DERSAL—The Story of Wildlife Conservation, 162

The Wonderful Wonders of One, Two, Three BY DAVID EUGENE SMITH—These Curious Numbers of Ours, 177

The Wonder World of Ants BY WILFRID S. BRONSON—What Is an Ant?, 115

The Wright Brothers BY QUENTIN REYNOLDS—Airplane in a Cow Pasture, 281

Zoo Expeditions BY WILLIAM BRIDGES—Journey for Elephants, 136

A World to Know BY JAMES S. TIPPETT—Bridges, 205

310

Subject Index

Adventure
    Airplane in a Cow Pasture *(The Wright Brothers)*, 281
    "Calling All Cars," 289
    Clipper Ship, 206
    Daring Voyage, A *(Robert Fulton)*, 272
    Journey for Elephants, 136
    Lion Adventures, 128
Africa
    Journey for Elephants, 136
    Lion Adventures, 128
Animals
    Circus Elephant, 158
    Four Little Foxes, 122
    Habits of the Hippopotamus, 157
    How to Tell the Wild Animals, 153
    Introducing Dinosaurs, 123
    Journey for Elephants, 136
    Lama, The, 155
    Land Animal That Went to Sea, The, 146
    Law of the Jungle, The, 159
    Lion Adventures, 128
    Panther, The, 155
    Story of Wildlife Conservation, The, 162
Atoms and Atomic Energy
    Atoms Are Like Letters, 220
    Scientists and the Bright Design, The, 170

Birds
    Bird, A, 93
    Bird Song, 92
    Children of the Wind, 90
    Couriers of the Sky, 94
    John James Audubon, 247
    John Muir Comes to America, 255
    Ostrich Is A Silly Bird, The, 156

    Something Told the Wild Geese, 86
    Story of Wildlife Conservation, The, 162
    Vulture, The, 156
Botanists
    Man-Made Plants *(Luther Burbank)*, 191
    Plant Peanuts *(George Washington Carver)*, 263
Bravery *(see* Character)
Bridges
    Bridges, 205
    Bridges Help Us Every Day, 197

Calendar
    Counting Moons, 180
Character
    BRAVERY
    Journey for Elephants, 136
    Lion Adventures, 128
    DETERMINATION
    Airplane in a Cow Pasture *(The Wright Brothers)*, 281
    Daring Voyage, A *(Robert Fulton)*, 272
    John James Audubon, 247
    New Light for the World *(Thomas Alva Edison)*, 225
    Plant Peanuts *(George Washington Carver)*, 263
    Rock That Glowed in the Dark, The *(Marie Curie)*, 214
    PATIENCE
    Daring Voyage, A *(Robert Fulton)*, 272
    John James Audubon, 247
    Journey for Elephants, 136
    Man-Made Plants *(Luther Burbank)*, 191
    Mr. Bell Invents the Telephone, 237

311

Character, PATIENCE *(cont.)*
  Plant Peanuts *(George Washington Carver),* 263
  PERSISTENCE
    Airplane in a Cow Pasture *(The Wright Brothers),* 281
    Daring Voyage, A *(Robert Fulton),* 272
    Mr. Bell Invents the Telephone, 237
    New Light for the World *(Thomas Alva Edison),* 225
    Plant Peanuts *(George Washington Carver),* 263
    Rock That Glowed in the Dark, The *(Marie Curie),* 214
Chemistry
  Chemistry Is Nature's Magic, 303
Clouds and Storms
  Cloud Zoo, 51
  How We Measure and Observe the Weather, 59
  Rain in Summer, 83
  Round-Trip to the Moon, 295
  Snowflakes, 87
  Storm, The, 52
Communication
  Bridges Help Us Every Day, 197
  "Calling All Cars," 289
  Mr. Bell Invents the Telephone, 237
  Round-Trip to the Moon, 295
Conservation
  John Muir Comes to America, 255
  Story of Wildlife Conservation, The, 162
Craftsmanship
  First Metal Workers, The, 186
  Johann Gutenberg and His Type, 244
  John James Audubon, 247

Determination *(see* Character)
Diving

Daring Voyage, A *(Robert Fulton),* 272
Ocean and Its Work, The, 10

Earth Formations
  Across Our Country, 3
  My Prairies, 7
  Scientists and the Bright Design, The, 170
  Volcanoes and Earthquakes, 18
Electricity and Electronics
  "Calling All Cars," 289
  Hundred Years of Inventions, A, 175
  Mr. Bell Invents the Telephone, 237
  New Light for the World *(Thomas Alva Edison),* 225
  Round-Trip to the Moon, 295
  Scientists and the Bright Design, The, 170
Engineering
  Airplane in a Cow Pasture *(The Wright Brothers),* 281
  Bridges Help Us Every Day, 197
  Daring Voyage, A *(Robert Fulton),* 272

Fables and Legends
  Butterfly and the Caterpillar, The, 100
  Counting Moons, 180
  First Metal Workers, The, 186
  Magic Mineral, A, 207
  Moon and Her Mother, The, 45
  Rivers and the Sea, The, 9
  Scientists and the Bright Design, The, 170
  These Curious Numbers of Ours, 177
  Thunder and Lightning, 54
Farming
  John Muir Comes to America, 255

312

Farming *(cont.)*
>   Man-Made Plants *(Luther Burbank)*, 191
>   Plant Peanuts *(George Washington Carver)*, 263

Fish
>   Ocean and Its Work, The, 10

Flying
>   Airplane in a Cow Pasture *(The Wright Brothers)*, 281
>   "Calling All Cars," 289
>   Hundred Years of Inventions, A, 175
>   Jet Propulsion, 301
>   Round-Trip to the Moon, 295

Fruit *(see* Trees)

Glass
>   Giant "Eyes," 28
>   To See the Very Small, 306

Gods and Goddesses
>   First Metal Workers, The, 186
>   Magic Mineral, A, 207
>   Thunder and Lightning, 54

Grafting
>   Man-Made Plants *(Luther Burbank)*, 191
>   Plant Peanuts *(George Washington Carver)*, 263

Humor and Nonsense
>   Butterfly and the Caterpillar, The, 100
>   Cloud Zoo, 51
>   Green Grass Growing All Around, The, 78
>   Habits of the Hippopotamus, 157
>   How to Tell the Wild Animals, 153
>   Lama, The, 155
>   My Private Natural History Museum, 166
>   Ostrich Is A Silly Bird, The, 156
>   Panther, The, 155
>   Vulture, The, 156

Hunting
>   John James Audubon, 247
>   John Muir Comes to America, 255
>   Journey for Elephants, 136
>   Law of the Jungle, The, 159
>   Lion Adventures, 128
>   Story of Wildlife Conservation, The, 162

Insects
>   Butterfly and the Caterpillar, The, 100
>   Insect Music, 102
>   Plant Peanuts *(George Washington Carver)*, 263
>   They Build with Wax, 108
>   To a Spider, 99
>   What Is an Ant?, 115

Inventors and Inventions
>   Airplane in a Cow Pasture *(The Wright Brothers)*, 281
>   Ben Franklin of Old Philadelphia, 234
>   Bridges Help Us Every Day, 197
>   "Calling All Cars," 289
>   Daring Voyage, A *(Robert Fulton)*, 272
>   First Metal Workers, The, 186
>   Giant "Eyes," 28
>   How We Measure and Observe the Weather, 59
>   Hundred Years of Inventions, A, 175
>   Jet Propulsion, 301
>   Johann Gutenberg and His Type, 244
>   Mr. Bell Invents the Telephone, 237
>   New Light for the World *(Thomas Alva Edison)*, 225
>   Round-Trip to the Moon, 295
>   Scientists and the Bright Design, The, 170
>   To See the Very Small, 306

Lava
    Across Our Country, 3
    Volcanoes and Earthquakes,
      18

Metals
    Bridges Help Us Every Day,
      197
    First Metal Workers, The, 186
    Johann Gutenberg and His
      Type, 244
Minerals
    First Metal Workers, The, 186
    Magic Mineral, A, 207
    Rock That Glowed in the Dark,
      The *(Marie Curie)*, 214
Molecules
    Atoms Are Like Letters, 220

Naturalists
    John James Audubon, 247
    John Muir Comes to America,
      255
    Man-Made Plants *(Luther Bur-
      bank)*, 191
    Plant Peanuts *(George Wash-
      ington Carver)*, 263
Nature
    Across Our Country, 3
    April Is a Dancer, 73
    Chemistry Is Nature's Magic,
      303
    Children of the Wind, 90
    Cloud Zoo, 51
    End of Summer Poem, 84
    Fog, 8
    Foolish Flowers, 82
    Frost Work, 88
    Heart of the Tree, The, 80
    How We Measure and Observe
      the Weather, 59
    How to Know the Trees, 74
    How to Tell the Wild Animals,
      153
    In Spring, 72
    John James Audubon, 247

John Muir Comes to America,
    255
June, 81
Land Animal That Went to Sea,
    The, 146
Law of the Jungle, The, 159
Let's Go to the Moon, 46
Man-Made Plants *(Luther Bur-
    bank)*, 191
Mist and All, The, 85
Months, The, 71
My Prairies, 7
Ocean and Its Work, The, 10
Plant Peanuts *(George Wash-
    ington Carver)*, 263
Portrait of the Sun, 37
Rain in Summer, 83
Seasons, The, 70
Silver, 44
Snowflakes, 87
Something Told the Wild
    Geese, 86
Stars, The, 30
Storm, The, 52
They Build with Wax, 108
Volcanoes and Earthquakes,
    18
Numbers
    These Curious Numbers of
      Ours, 177

Ocean and the Sea
    Clipper Ship, 206
    Daring Voyage, A *(Robert Ful-
      ton)*, 272
    Land Animal That Went to Sea,
      The, 146
    Ocean and Its Work, The, 10
    Rivers and the Sea, The, 9

Palomar Observatory
    Giant "Eyes," 28
Patience (*see* Character)
Persistence (*see* Character)
Poetry and Songs
    April Is a Dancer, 73

Poetry and Songs *(cont.)*
    Bird, A, 93
    Bird Song, 92
    Bridges, 205
    Butterfly and the Caterpillar, The, 100
    Children of the Wind, 90
    Circus Elephant, 158
    Clipper Ship, 206
    Cloud Zoo, 51
    End of Summer Poem, 84
    Fog, 8
    Foolish Flowers, 82
    Four Little Foxes, 122
    Frost Work, 88
    Green Grass Growing All Around, The, 78
    Habits of the Hippopotamus, 157
    Heart of the Tree, The, 80
    How to Tell the Wild Animals, 153
    In Spring, 72
    June, 81
    Lama, The, 155
    Law of the Jungle, The, 159
    Mist and All, The, 85
    Months, The, 71
    My Prairies, 7
    Ostrich Is A Silly Bird, The, 156
    Panther, The, 155
    Rain in Summer, 83
    Seasons, The, 70
    Silver, 44
    Snowflakes, 87
    Something Told the Wild Geese, 86
    Storm, The, 52
    To a Spider, 99
    Vulture, The, 156
    World Stands Out on Either Side, The, 2

Reptiles
    Introducing Dinosaurs, 123

    Snakes, 120
Rocks and Sand
    Across Our Country, 3
    First Metal Workers, The, 186
    Introducing Dinosaurs, 123
    Magic Mineral, A, 207
    Ocean and Its Work, The, 10
    Rock That Glowed in the Dark, The *(Marie Curie)*, 214
    Volcanoes and Earthquakes, 18

Science and Scientists
    Airplane in a Cow Pasture *(The Wright Brothers)*, 281
    Ben Franklin of Old Philadelphia, 234
    "Calling All Cars," 289
    Counting Moons, 180
    Jet Propulsion, 301
    Man-Made Plants *(Luther Burbank)*, 191
    New Light for the World *(Thomas Alva Edison)*, 225
    Plant Peanuts *(George Washington Carver)*, 263
    Rock That Glowed in the Dark, The *(Marie Curie)*, 214
    Round-Trip to the Moon, 295
    Scientists and the Bright Design, The, 170
    To See the Very Small, 306
Seasons
    April Is a Dancer, 73
    Counting Moons, 180
    End of Summer Poem, 84
    Frost Work, 88
    In Spring, 72
    June, 81
    Mist and All, The, 85
    Months, The, 71
    Plant Peanuts *(George Washington Carver)*, 263
    Rain in Summer, 83
    Seasons, The, 70
    Snowflakes, 87

Seasons *(cont.)*
    Something Told the Wild
      Geese, 86
    Story of Wildlife Conservation,
      The, 162
    They Build with Wax, 108
Ships
    "Calling All Cars," 289
    Clipper Ship, 206
    Daring Voyage, A *(Robert Fulton),* 272
    Ocean and Its Work, The, 10
    Stars, The, 30
Submarines
    Daring Voyage, A *(Robert Fulton),* 272
Sun, Moon and Stars
    Counting Moons, 180
    Giant "Eyes," 28
    Let's Go to the Moon, 46
    Moon and Her Mother, The, 45
    Portrait of the Sun, 37
    Round-Trip to the Moon, 295
    Stars, The, 30

Transportation
    Airplane in a Cow Pasture *(The Wright Brothers),* 281
    Bridges, 205
    Bridges Help Us Every Day, 197

"Calling All Cars," 289
Clipper Ship, 206
Daring Voyage, A *(Robert Fulton),* 272
John Muir Comes to America, 255
Trees
    Heart of the Tree, The, 80
    How to Know the Trees, 74
    John Muir Comes to America, 255
    Man-Made Plants *(Luther Burbank),* 191

Uranium
    Rock That Glowed in the Dark, The *(Marie Curie),* 214

Volcanoes and Earthquakes
    First Metal Workers, The, 186
    Volcanoes and Earthquakes, 18

Weather
    "Calling All Cars," 289
    Frost Work, 88
    How We Measure and Observe the Weather, 59
    Insect Music, 102
    Mist and All, The, 85
    Rain in Summer, 83
    Round-Trip to the Moon, 295
    Snowflakes, 87

Illustrators

Alexandroff, D., 74, 88, 94, 108, 191
Bice, Clare, 205
Bileck, Marvin, 37
Bobritzky, George, 2, 3, 197
Bronson, Wilfrid S., 102, 115
Caputo, Mauro, 28, 175
Carter, Helene, 180
Cellini, Joseph, 99, 128
Clement, Charles, 220, 303
Coggins, Jack, 46
Crichlow, Ernest, 7, 207, 263
Danska, Herbert, 247
Daugherty, Charles M., 170
Davis, Bette J., 289, 295
Eichenberg, Fritz, 234
Fleishman, Seymour, 54, 225
Frankenberg, Robert, 122, 162
Goldstein, Henry, 136
Hollerbach, Serge, 237, 301
Keats, Ezra Jack, 1, 10, 59, 69, 89, 90, 169, 186, 244

Kimball, Sabra Mallett, 92, 93
Landau, Emma, 30, 159
Landau, Jacob, 281
Lawson, Robert, 86, 87
Leighton, Clare, 158
Metzl, Ervine, 156, 157
Mill, Eleanor, 214, 255
Miret, Gil, 8, 9, 306
Perl, Susan, 52, 166
Sand, Elaine, 120
Saynor, Marjorie, 177
Sendak, Maurice, 153, 155
Simon, Howard, 272
Stern, Marie, 72-73, 78, 80
Symonds, Kenneth, 177, 179
Tanner, Barbara, 70, 71, 85, 100
Thompson, Mozelle, 44, 45, 51, 82, 83
Voter, Thomas W., 123, 146
Wiese, Kurt, 18
Wong, Jeanyee, 81

317

Index

Title and AUTHOR:

Across Our Country, CARROLL LANE FENTON AND MILDRED ADAMS FENTON, 3

AESOP, *The Moon and Her Mother,* 45
The Rivers and the Sea, 9

Airplane in a Cow Pasture, QUENTIN REYNOLDS, 281

AKELEY, CARL AND MARY L. J., *Lion Adventures,* 128

ANDREWS, ROY CHAPMAN, *Introducing Dinosaurs,* 123
The Land Animal That Went to Sea, 146

April Is a Dancer (Poem), SOLVEIG PAULSON RUSSELL, 73

Atoms Are Like Letters, JEROME S. MEYER, 220

BARRY, CATHERINE E., *Giant "Eyes,"* 28

BEELER, NELSON F., AND FRANKLYN M. BRANLEY, *Jet Propulsion,* 301

BELLOC, HILAIRE, *The Vulture* (Poem), 156

Ben Franklin of Old Philadelphia, MARGARET COUSINS, 234

BENNETT, ROWENA, *End of Summer Poem,* 84

Bird, A (Poem), EMILY DICKINSON, 93

Bird Song (Poem), LAURA E. RICHARDS, 92

BONNER, MARY GRAHAM, *Couriers of the Sky,* 94

BRETZ, RUDOLPH, *The Ocean and Its Work,* 10

Bridges (Poem), JAMES S. TIPPETT, 205

Bridges Help Us Every Day, DAVID B. STEINMAN, 197

BRIDGES, WILLIAM, *Journey for Elephants,* 136

BRINDZE, RUTH, *Counting Moons,* 180

BRONSON, WILFRID S., *Insect Music,* 102
What Is an Ant?, 115

BUNNER, H. C., *The Heart of the Tree* (Poem), 80

Butterfly and the Caterpillar, The (Poem), JOSEPH LAUREN, 100

"Calling All Cars," JACK GOULD, 289

318

Chemistry Is Nature's Magic, JEROME S. MEYER, 303

Children of the Wind (Poem), CARL SANDBURG, 90

Circus Elephant (Poem), KATHRYN WORTH, 158

CLARK, G. GLENWOOD, *New Light for the World,* 225

Clipper Ship (Poem), NANCY BYRD TURNER, 206

Cloud Zoo (Poem), NORMA GILLETT, 51

Counting Moons, RUTH BRINDZE, 180

Couriers of the Sky, MARY GRAHAM BONNER, 94

COUSINS, MARGARET, *Ben Franklin of Old Philadelphia,* 234

CRESSON, ABIGAIL, *To a Spider* (Poem), 99

Daring Voyage, A, RALPH NADING HILL, 272

DE LA MARE, WALTER, *Silver* (Poem), 44

DICKINSON, EMILY, *A Bird* (Poem), 93

DUFFY, NONA KEEN, *Frost Work* (Poem), 88

End of Summer Poem, ROWENA BENNETT, 84

EPSTEIN, SAM AND BERYL, *Johann Gutenberg and His Type,* 244

FENTON, CARROLL LANE AND MILDRED ADAMS FENTON, *Across Our Country,* 3

FIELD, RACHEL, *Something Told the Wild Geese* (Poem), 86

First Metal Workers, The, GRACE KINER, 186

Fog (Poem), CARL SANDBURG, 8

Foolish Flowers (Poem), RUPERT SARGENT HOLLAND, 82

Four Little Foxes (Poem), LEW SARETT, 122

FREEMAN, MARY E. W., *The Ostrich Is A Silly Bird* (Poem), 156

Frost Work (Poem), NONA KEEN DUFFY, 88

GARLAND, HAMLIN, *My Prairies* (Poem), 7

Giant "Eyes," CATHERINE E. BARRY, 28

GILLETT, NORMA, *Cloud Zoo* (Poem), 51

GOULD, JACK, *"Calling All Cars,"* 289

Round-Trip to the Moon, 295

GRAHAM, EDWARD H., AND WILLIAM R. VAN DERSAL, *The Story of Wildlife Conservation,* 162

319

Green Grass Growing All Around, The, OLD RHYME, 78

GUITERMAN, ARTHUR, *Habits of the Hippopotamus* (Poem), 157

Habits of the Hippopotamus (Poem), ARTHUR GUITERMAN, 157

Heart of the Tree, The (Poem), H. C. BUNNER, 80

HEILE, MARYANNA, *Thunder and Lightning,* 54

HILL, RALPH NADING, *A Daring Voyage,* 272

HOFFMAN, ALICE CROWELL, *June* (Poem), 81

HOGBEN, LANCELOT, *A Hundred Years of Inventions,* 175

HOLLAND, RUPERT SARGENT, *Foolish Flowers* (Poem), 82

How to Know the Trees, MILLICENT E. SELSAM, 74

How to Tell the Wild Animals (Poem), CAROLYN WELLS, 153

How We Measure and Observe the Weather, IVAN RAY TANNE-HILL, 59

Hundred Years of Inventions, A, LANCELOT HOGBEN, 175

Insect Music, WILFRID S. BRONSON, 102

In Spring (Poem), MICHAEL LEWIS, 72

Introducing Dinosaurs, ROY CHAPMAN ANDREWS, 123

Jet Propulsion, NELSON F. BEELER AND FRANKLYN M. BRANLEY, 301

Johann Gutenberg and His Type, SAM AND BERYL EPSTEIN, 244

John James Audubon, MARGARET AND JOHN KIERAN, 247

John Muir Comes to America, CHARLES NORMAN, 255

Journey for Elephants, WILLIAM BRIDGES, 136

June (Poem), ALICE CROWELL HOFFMAN, 81

KIERAN, MARGARET AND JOHN, *John James Audubon,* 247

KINER, GRACE, *The First Metal Workers,* 186

KIPLING, RUDYARD, *The Law of the Jungle* (Poem), 159

Lama, The (Poem), OGDEN NASH, 155

Land Animal That Went to Sea, The, ROY CHAPMAN ANDREWS, 146

LAUREN, JOSEPH, *The Butterfly and the Caterpillar* (Poem), 100

Law of the Jungle, The (Poem), RUDYARD KIPLING, 159

Let's Go to the Moon, ARMAND SPITZ, 46

LEWIS, MICHAEL, *In Spring* (Poem), 72

Lion Adventures, CARL AND MARY L. J. AKELEY, 128

LOFTING, HUGH, *My Private Natural History Museum*, 166

LONGFELLOW, HENRY WADSWORTH, *Rain in Summer* (Poem), 83

    Snowflakes (Poem), 87

Magic Mineral, A, LILIAN HOLMES STRACK, 207

Man-Made Plants, JANET MCGILL, 191

MCGILL, JANET, *Man-Made Plants*, 191

MEYER, JEROME S., *Atoms Are Like Letters*, 220

    Chemistry Is Nature's Magic, 303

    The Stars, 30

MILLAY, EDNA ST. VINCENT, *The World Stands Out on Either Side* (Poem), 2

Mist and All, The (Poem), DIXIE WILLSON, 85

Months, The (Poem), CHRISTINA ROSSETTI, 71

Moon and Her Mother, The, AESOP, 45

Mr. Bell Invents the Telephone, KATHERINE B. SHIPPEN, 237

My Prairies (Poem), HAMLIN GARLAND, 7

My Private Natural History Museum, HUGH LOFTING, 166

NASH, OGDEN, *The Lama* (Poem), 155

    The Panther (Poem), 155

New Light for the World, G. GLENWOOD CLARK, 225

NORMAN, CHARLES, *John Muir Comes to America*, 255

Ocean and Its Work, The, RUDOLPH BRETZ, 10

Ostrich Is A Silly Bird, The (Poem), MARY E. W. FREEMAN, 156

Panther, The (Poem), OGDEN NASH, 155

Plant Peanuts, ANNE TERRY WHITE, 263

Portrait of the Sun, ANNE TERRY WHITE, 37

Rain in Summer (Poem), HENRY WADSWORTH LONGFELLOW, 83

REED, MAXWELL W., *Volcanoes and Earthquakes*, 18

REYNOLDS, QUENTIN, *Airplane in a Cow Pasture,* 281

RICHARDS, LAURA E., *Bird Song* (Poem), 92

Rivers and the Sea, The, AESOP, 9

Rock That Glowed in the Dark, The, LILIAN HOLMES STRACK, 214

ROSSETTI, CHRISTINA, *The Months* (Poem), 71

Round-Trip to the Moon, JACK GOULD, 295

RUSSELL, SOLVEIG PAULSON, *April Is a Dancer* (Poem), 73

SANDBURG, CARL, *Children of the Wind* (Poem), 90
> *Fog* (Poem), 8

SARETT, LEW, *Four Little Foxes* (Poem), 122

SCHWARTZ, JULIUS, *To See the Very Small,* 306

Scientists and the Bright Design, The, KATHERINE B. SHIPPEN, 170

Seasons, The (Poem), EDNA L. STERLING, 70

SELSAM, MILLICENT E., *How to Know the Trees,* 74

SHIPPEN, KATHERINE B., *Mr. Bell Invents the Telephone,* 237
> *The Scientists and the Bright Design,* 170

Silver (Poem), WALTER DE LA MARE, 44

SMITH, DAVID EUGENE, *These Curious Numbers of Ours,* 177

Snakes, HERBERT S. ZIM, 120

Snowflakes (Poem), HENRY WADSWORTH LONGFELLOW, 87

Something Told the Wild Geese (Poem), RACHEL FIELD, 86

SPITZ, ARMAND, *Let's Go to the Moon,* 46

Stars, The, JEROME S. MEYER, 30

STEINMAN, DAVID B., *Bridges Help Us Every Day,* 197

STERLING, DOROTHY, *They Build with Wax,* 108

STERLING, EDNA L., *The Seasons* (Poem), 70

Storm, The (Poem), RICHARD AND LOUIS UNTERMEYER, 52

Story of Wildlife Conservation, The, EDWARD H. GRAHAM AND WILLIAM R. VAN DERSAL, 162

STRACK, LILIAN HOLMES, *A Magic Mineral,* 207
> *The Rock That Glowed in the Dark,* 214

TANNEHILL, IVAN RAY, *How We Measure and Observe the Weather*, 59

These Curious Numbers of Ours, DAVID EUGENE SMITH, 177

They Build with Wax, DOROTHY STERLING, 108

Thunder and Lightning, MARYANNA HEILE, 54

TIPPETT, JAMES S., *Bridges* (Poem), 205

To a Spider (Poem), ABIGAIL CRESSON, 99

To See the Very Small, JULIUS SCHWARTZ, 306

TURNER, NANCY BYRD, *Clipper Ship* (Poem), 206

UNTERMEYER, RICHARD AND LOUIS, *The Storm* (Poem), 52

Volcanoes and Earthquakes, W. MAXWELL REED, 18

Vulture, The (Poem), HILAIRE BELLOC, 156

WELLS, CAROLYN, *How to Tell the Wild Animals* (Poem), 153

What Is an Ant?, WILFRID S. BRONSON, 115

WHITE, ANNE TERRY, *Plant Peanuts*, 263

　　Portrait of the Sun, 37

WILLSON, DIXIE, *The Mist and All* (Poem), 85

World Stands Out on Either Side, The (Poem), EDNA ST. VINCENT MILLAY, 2

WORTH, KATHRYN, *Circus Elephant* (Poem), 158

ZIM, HERBERT S., *Snakes*, 120